W9-CQT-482

Girlfriend to Girlfriend: A Fertility Companion

Girlfriend to Girlfriend: A Fertility Companion

by Kristen Magnacca

Copyright © 2000 by Kristen Magnacca

All rights reserved.
No part of this book may be reproduced, stored in a retrieval
system, or transmitted by any means, electronic, mechanical,
photocopying, recording, or otherwise, without written
permission from the author.

ISBN: 1-58820-213-5

1stBooks – rev. 10/9/00

This book is dedicated to Cole, my cherub.

The greatest use of life is to spend it for something that will outlast it.

William James (1842-1910)

Acknowledgments

I would like to begin by thanking my husband, Mark, for his willingness to so blatantly share our fertility issues. I love him for sharing our intimate story with others for the sole purpose of easing others' pain. Without Mark's support and encouragement, I believe that this book would not have been a reality.

Thanks also to our family for their constant prayers and unconditional support and to my Rosebud, who always knows the right words to push me through my doubts; my Ana Paula for being my rock; Maria and Luke for their friendship and for being our partners in fertility. And to the Original Five for sharing my rain and sunshine.

My friend and neighbor, Sarah, who introduced me to Maryellen who in turn introduced me to Janet McCartney, my editor. Janet's professionalism, detail orientation and ability to ask wonderful questions propelled *Girlfriend to Girlfriend* to a different level.

Dr. Robert Robinson who has provided me with numerous "moment's insights" when most needed. Dr. R. Ian Hardy of the Fertility Center of New England who provided exceptional medical care, patience, understanding, compassion and rays of hope when doubt was rampant.

Dr. Herbert Benson and Dr. Ali Domar of the Beth Israel Deaconess Medical Center's Behavioral Medicine Program for Infertility for being my angels of light. They don't call Ali the goddess of fertility for nothing!

Dede Dunbar for her ability to "see" which brought comfort, strength and a different level of understanding.

vii

Introduction

Never, never, never, never give up.
Winston Churchill (1874-1965)

It's 2:09 AM and the total darkness of our bedroom is pierced by the green glow of our bedside alarm clock. It's 2:09 AM, and I've been awake for three hours staring into the darkness. The warmth of Mark's body invites me to snuggle in closer and adds comfort to the chill that runs up my spine. The rhythm of his breath gives a beat to the chant in my head.

I can't believe they're pregnant. (inhale) I can't believe I'm not. (exhale) What is wrong with us? (inhale) What is happening to me? (exhale)

Thank God for Mark. I don't think I would have made the drive home today without him. He talked me in as if he was landing a 747 filled with precious cargo.

"Mark, I just want a baby. I don't understand. What is wrong with us that we cannot conceive? Everyone else can have a child!"

Mark's loving tone never showed his concern.

"I'm sorry, honey, I'm so sorry," he repeated over and over again.

Mark and I had planned our future together so precisely. Our wedding was a beautiful celebration of our love for each other and the joy of finding our soul mates. I sold my preschool/daycare business and moved across the state to be with my husband.

It was a fairy tale. I would work with Mark, conceive our wonderful baby and then concentrate on raising our family. At thirty-three I was longing to be pregnant and carry our child. But as the months evaporated, we marked the passing of time and opportunity with white wands with one purple line.

Had I waited too long to join the ranks of motherhood? Instead of focusing my attention on caring for other women's babies, should I have focused on creating my own? Then, there was the doubt brought on by the drug DES. My mom had been in danger of miscarrying and had been given this drug to remain pregnant. Years later, it was shown to cause infertility in adult daughters of women who took it when pregnant.

This was all a tiny whisper of concern in the back of my mind. But it wasn't until today with my two pregnant friends that the volume of my concern was increased and I was struck with the feeling that I might never have a baby. The day started out with me talking to my friend Mary's young daughter.

"Guess what?" Elizabeth's tiny voice bellowed out excitement.

"What, honey?" I replied.

"My mom is gonna have a baby!" she screamed.

I felt the instant need to run to our bathroom and become violently ill. "Oh wow! How exciting for your family!" I squeezed out.

"Kristen, are you OK?" Mary was back on the phone.

"I'm so happy for you, Mary, I didn't realize you were trying again."

"It's a surprise to us," she confirmed.

I felt as though the phone shot a bullet through my head. I flinched away from it as a form of protection.

We finalized our plans and decided to meet in the lobby of the Four Seasons Hotel.

The overhead blast of hot air warmed my path as I greeted the uniformed doorman with a smile. He ushered me through the heavy glass revolving door into the spectacular lobby that left me standing with my mouth gaping wide open. The carpet sank under my feet as I chose the perfect people-watching spot. Within moments, Mary appeared. As soon as I saw her, my envy melted away and I gave her a congratulatory hug. We released each other from our greeting and spotted Svetlana hurrying across the street. She was so meticulously dressed; her clothing screamed "city dweller."

Our reservations weren't for another hour, so we browsed the hotel gift shop, then climbed the curving staircase to the upper ladies' room. Svetlana went to the vanity to wash her hands and apply lipstick and I settled into the upholstered stool next to her. She looked flawless in her long, flowing dark skirt and matching black blazer. Then my eyes fell to her waist and my skin grew cold.

She was pregnant. I knew she was pregnant.

As soon as the thought popped into my head, I willed it away. You're paranoid, I told myself. Of course she isn't pregnant!

We made our way back to the lobby and resumed our wait for the table. I thought if we made our presence known they would call us more quickly.

The plush lobby exuded wealth with its mahogany tables, wood paneling, large grandfather clocks and exquisite flower arrangements. The flames in the fireplace danced in the breeze from the opening door while fresh flowers stood in direct contrast to the dead of winter outside.

We were standing in a triangle, each of us a point, when our conversation turned to Mary's pregnancy.

"Wouldn't it be wonderful if we all could be pregnant together!" Mary spoke with excitement. Then meekly, Svetlana said, "Well, I'm sorta pregnant, too."

Our triangle blurred into a circular motion. The room began to spin at the same rate of speed. My knees felt as though they would no longer support my weight. I was concentrated on holding back my tears and stabilizing my balance when I heard a male voice calling us for our table.

"I just need to make it to our table and then through brunch and I can retreat to the safety of my house," I told myself.

I've always considered myself to be a strong person. I started my own business, a preschool/daycare, when I was 22 and built it into a thriving business with 50 children and 18 staff members. I had risen through the ranks of the board of directors of my city's Chamber of Commerce and was the third woman chairman of the board. I always had specific goals and objectives and knew how to achieve them. So why all of a sudden couldn't I do what was so natural, to become pregnant and have a baby? Over the past months I had become a shadow of the stable, level-headed Kristen; I was now a woman whose every thought led her back to her childlessness.

I never entertained the thought that my quest for our child would lead me to the darkest night of my soul. I would lose my faith in my body, my mind, my marriage and my God.

I was in foreign territory. The extreme land of infertility promises hope with no guarantee of delivering.

It was only with extreme focus and determination that I made it through brunch without collapsing. I said my good-byes to my friends and paced while waiting for the valet to bring me my car. The wait proved to be too long and I broke down as I spotted the headlights to my vehicle. Safely inside, I lost control and reached for the phone to call Mark as I began my long drive home.

Girlfriend to Girlfriend:
"Sometimes a moment's insight is worth a lifetime's experience."

That quote has to be one of my favorites. Oliver Wendell Holmes wrote of a moment's insight... how I longed for that moment's insight when my husband, Mark, and I started on the road to discover what was impeding our efforts to conceive a child.

We set out trying to conceive our child the natural way and ended up at the hands of ART (Assisted Reproductive Technology). According to the Center for Disease Control and Prevention's 1995 Assisted Reproductive Technology Success Rates Report, ART is defined as "All treatments or procedures that involve the handling of human eggs and sperm for the purpose of establishing a pregnancy. Types of ART include IVF, GIFT, ZIFT, embryo cryopreservation, egg or embryo donation and surrogate birth."

I was totally overwhelmed with the alphabet soup and with each step further into ART's world, I craved knowledge, understanding, and, most importantly, companionship.

The world of assisted reproductive technology, or ART's world as I refer to it in this book, has its own culture and set of mores. Our journey through it was like traveling to a foreign land without a travel guide.

The majority of the wonderful books that I read about the procedures felt very clinical in nature and left me missing the sisterly relationship that only another "having trouble conceiving" woman could offer.

If you and I could have a heart to heart visit regarding our fertility issues, it would surely be in my comfy living room with a hot cup of tea. In its place I would like to offer you this book. Each chapter contains at least one Girlfriend to Girlfriend section, containing helpful hints and the lowdown of my experiences.

Chapter One
Looking for ART in All the Wrong Places

A journey of a thousand miles begins with a single step.
Lao Tzu (6th century B.C.)

I was born on May 23, 1963, under the sign of Gemini, the twin. My zodiac coding already predestined me to have two distinctive personalities. First, there was the steadfast, responsible, considerate, patient, and logical twin and second, the emotional, scattered, fun-loving, short-tempered twin.

I had discarded the logical twin months ago along with each little white plastic wand displaying only one single purple line.

The emotional Gemini was in full force... long gone was the sensible, stable, reasonable Kristen. I was running on pure emotion.

The repeated question of who I was becoming pounded in my head. Who am I? What is the problem? Why can't we become pregnant? The repetitive pounding began to shake my senses and made my eyes hurt from the inside out. Closing my eyes and shaking my head from left to right was the only remedy to stop my inner noise.

I needed to concentrate on the tasks at hand. The office that my husband and I shared was empty. The quiet hum of the computers was interrupted with an occasional ring of the telephone. I had spread out my files for review in Mark's office. As I pored over the pending work, a twinge shot across my lower back and I shifted my weight in the chair. "I have been sitting in this position for a while," I said out loud, quickly glancing around to see if anyone heard me. To my relief, I realized I was alone.

My attention drifted to the traffic speeding by our brick office building. From my vantage point I could look down into the passing cars. My eyes quickly picked out the cars with children's seats in them. I began counting and wondering. I wonder if we were successful this month? It was the day my menstrual cycle was to begin and as I looked outside I saw five

1

or six cars containing children's seats pass by. In my mind's eye I could see our car with an infant carrier tucked safety in the back seat with the child mirror adjusted so that I would be able to watch our baby rest while I drove to our destination.

I snapped out of my daydream and began completing the calls necessary to secure the proper transfers of funds for our client's investments. Another interruption, this one definitely recognizable and unavoidable. The sun from the window cast my shadow on the opposite wall as I stood. I quickened my movement, around the desk, through the door, down the hall past the reception area, where I opened the wooden office door, en route to the ladies' room.

We weren't pregnant. I felt the bathroom walls close in on me. My knees buckled as I began to splash cold water onto my face in an attempt to splash me back in control.

I retraced my steps back to Mark's office in a zombie-like state. My concentration was gone. Glancing at the clock I realized I would not be able to reach Mark now, I would bear this month's disappointment alone for now, longer than was comfortable.

Mark was at an appointment with a client, probably engrossed in his evangelism of the proper use of a living trust. The word *trust* sent a stream of anger through my body.

I didn't trust my body or myself. How could I trust my body? It had stood me up for months, no, for years. We had been in a courting ritual. I was doing all the appropriate tasks at the appropriate times and still my body left me there, waiting with disappointment and despair. It had drawn its battle lines and slowly became the enemy.

In that instant, I reached for the telephone and called two floors up. "Is Dr. S in today?" I asked. The reply, "Yes," went off in my head like a gun for the start of a marathon. I was off again, around my desk through the door, down the hall past the reception area, opening the wooden door out into the hallway, and running at full speed up two flights of stairs.

The nurse was just hanging up her telephone when I tapped at her glass window. "I need to see Dr. S," I said, referring to our primary care physician, who was a recent graduate into full doctorhood. He was my age and knew both Mark and I as patients and neighbors.

"Just a moment, Kristen, he's with a patient."

I looked at the nurse and choked back my tears. "I need to see him now," I whispered, my voice cracking.

Dr. S appeared from around the corner and ushered me into his office. Using a fatherly tone, he began.

"Kristen, you and Mark are in great health, you really haven't been trying that long. It takes the average couple six to nine months to conceive."

"We're well over that," I snapped.

"Kristen, I know how much you want a child, but give it a few more months and then come back."

The response and answers that I desperately needed were not forthcoming. This exchange was getting me nowhere.

"I understand what you're saying, thanks." I lifted myself from the chair and went home for the day. Sitting in my driveway, with my head resting on the steering wheel, I couldn't recall any of the drive home.

I just wanted the pain and hurt to be replaced with pure joy, the joy of pregnancy.

ART, ART, where art thou?

I wanted to be pregnant yesterday or the day before that! Just like so many of my friends were. I had lived through their first pregnancies and now watched in envy as they expanded themselves and their families for a second time.

My primary care physician's response to my outcry sent me running into another doctor's stirrups. I totally disregarded an appointment that I had scheduled to take place in three months' time with a reproductive endocrinologist referred to us by my nurse midwife, the woman who performs my annual gynecological exams. I was not about to sit around and wait for three months while my eggs were aging!

Instead, with a referral from my friend Mary, I made an appointment with her doctor. Mary was currently pregnant with her third child, and in very different circumstances than we were.

Her doctor was well trained and had wonderful credentials in assuming the position and at catching babies as they entered into the world the natural way. However, I was having difficulties procreating the normal way. He was the wrong choice for our circumstances. But at the time, I was in such an emotional state I didn't have the ability to recognize this.

So Mark and I hurried into Boston for my appointment with Dr. Wrong, which conveniently was the last one of the day. As we stopped at the entrance, I leapt out of the car and glanced over my shoulder and smiled at Mark as he pulled away to park the car.

I quickened my pace and rushed down the entry hall, unaware of other patients also proceeding on their way to their appointments. With my heart pounding and my adrenaline pumping, I found Dr. Wrong's office. We were running late. This is usual for us, though, despite my best efforts, because my husband suffers from time distortion: an event that logically would take say, ten or fifteen minutes, Mark assumes would take three minutes. This is a very unnerving habit for the anal Kristen.

I opened the door to a waiting room packed with women. As I registered with the receptionist, I felt the entire room's attention now focused on me.

Where's Mark? I thought. I really need his support.

"I'm Kristen Magnacca, a new patient to see Dr. Wrong," I whispered. The nurse responded to me in a very loud voice.

"First time here? You're going to have to fill out this paperwork, what's your insurance? Are you pregnant?"

I replied a weak, "No." Where the hell is Mark? "We need some assistance in becoming pregnant," I whispered again, hoping she would follow my lead and lower her voice.

"Having troubles conceiving." I watched her mouth scream these words. "Take a seat and return the completed paperwork to me."

My God, I thought as I turned around and noticed that all eyes were upon me. I quickly put down my head and took the seat behind the office door. Each time the door swung open I

4

brought my feet closer to me. It looked as though I was in a sitting fetal position. Where the hell is Mark?

I completed the paperwork and returned it to nurse "Big Mouth" and when I turned this time to return to my seat, Mark was walking in the door.

"Where have you been?" I snapped.

"The parking garage was filled."

"I'm glad you're here now," I replied.

I had been so immersed in filling the paperwork out that this was the first chance I had to glance around the room. It was the first time I noticed how dreary it was. The dark gray carpet showed its wear, looking tired as it spanned the room and climbed part way up the receptionist's booth. The focal point of the room was a patchwork quilt thumbtacked to the wall. Someone needs to give that quilt a good thrashing; the dust on it has to be an inch thick, I thought to myself.

As my glance shifted to the left, I suddenly noticed the stomachs of the line of women sitting on my side. They were in all stages of pregnancy. Six months, I guessed, nine months, four months. I suddenly felt nauseous. I found myself fixated on their stomachs.

Each time their names were called I stared as they lifted their pregnant bodies out of their chairs and rearranged themselves, walking as if they had just gotten off a horse. I strained to look around the corner and followed them with my gaze until they were out of sight. I looked down at my flat stomach and began to rub my stomach in a circular motion as a form of comfort. With the great longing I had, I too wanted to have an extended stomach, mu-mu shirts, and our child growing inside me.

Finally, it was our turn to see the doctor. The receptionist led us to an office where Dr. Wrong sat behind his desk. While closing a file he spun around in his chair and greeted us.

"I'm Doctor Wrong," he said as he first shook Mark's hand and then mine. I took the chair across from the doctor and Mark sat to my right. I did a visual check of the office. His desk faced the window, with pictures of his children and himself. I made a mental note, no mother or women in these pictures. He must be divorced, I thought as I played detective. The office was well organized but cold and sterile (no pun intended).

During our short conversation he never even looked at Mark, which at the time I thought was because he was trying to build rapport with me. Later on I realized that this had been a huge indication as to how he would treat us as a couple. He didn't. He focused only on me, the woman, and Mark was just there.

Then he brought us into the examining room, asked me to disrobe for an internal examination, and promptly disappeared. I decided to ignore the feelings of doubt and proceed.

Trying not to think, I systematically removed my pants and undies and put on the johnny. I felt way out of my comfort zone. I was here on a reconnaissance mission, supposedly to just meet this doctor and now I found myself naked from the waist down. As I took my position on the examination table, the paper beneath me made a crumpling sound. "This doctor will help you have a child," I said to myself. I decided to ignore the voice of doubt and proceed.

This was Mark's first time in a gynecologist's office and he was unsure as to where he should stand or sit. He finally stopped at the countertop and stood as though he was a wooden soldier. His behavior reminded me of my dog Koko, who would spin in circles until she felt she was in the proper place to rest. Like Koko, Mark was also searching for the proper, respectful place to rest. The examination room was tiny and it was difficult for him or anyone to be unobtrusive in these tight quarters.

If I weren't the one living this episode, it would have been funny. It reminded me of a scene from *Candid Camera*. It was our *This is Your Life* with none of the feel-good parts yet. I began to feel the chill of the cool air against my naked lower back when the doctor returned. He did a quick pelvic examination, took a Pap smear, and then pushed his chair and himself away from my private area. The next words out of his mouth were that he would schedule me for a hysterosalpingogram – a procedure, he explained, where the doctor shoots dye into the uterus and Fallopian tubes to check for blockages.

As I blinked my eyes to focus on him and his announcement, he was gone. I slid off the examination table with my feet landing on the cold tile floor. I felt violated. But I was still slightly optimistic that we had begun to determine what was blocking our ability to conceive.

We were naïve, not realizing how far we were from achieving our family and where our quest for our baby would lead us.

Mark, Mark, what did he say? A hystrowhatagram? "Mark, go get him and ask him what the hell is he talking about." Mark followed him out the door, while I quickly put on my underwear and pants. I could hear him discussing the date and time with Dr. W.

It turned out to be two weeks later that I was again naked from the waist down, waiting at a lab for Dr. Wrong to arrive for the hysterosalpingogram. This test needed to be performed between days two to ten of my menstrual cycle.

I was lying on an antique-looking piece of medical equipment; it was a X-ray machine with stirrups on each side. "If you think I can get my legs open that wide, you must be crazy," I said to the lab technician. She laughed and swung the stirrups in so that I could assume the position. She then went through the procedure of the test and told me to ask any questions that I might have.

"May I have a copy of the X-rays?" I asked the lab technician. She said sure. Why I wanted them I didn't quite understand – a strange keepsake on the way to our baby, I guess. I then asked, "How often do you work with Dr. Wrong?"

"Oh, not that often," she replied. This should have been a red flag.

It was 11:20 AM and Dr. Wrong was now twenty minutes late. I was already lying on the table and propped myself up to greet him as he stopped abruptly at my open legs and started the procedure. He was definitely lacking in bedside manner. Mark and I began to focus on a TV screen that would display my inner workings.

I then noticed that Dr. W. seemed annoyed. I initially thought that he might have been up late the night before, delivering a baby to some blessed woman. I shook my head to dissolve that image.

The sound of cracking knuckles brought me back to my reality. Dr. Wrong had just inserted a plastic speculum into my vagina. Then he followed that with a flexible catheter and wove it into my cervix and up to my Fallopian tubes. The catheter is only the size of one of those drink box straws but the image of a green garden hose popped into my head. The doctor had described this procedure as "minor discomfort" and based on this, I certainly didn't want to go through major discomfort.

I felt myself leave my body and fly to the beach in Saint Croix where I had vacationed with a girlfriend of mine. There in the sunshine, I relaxed, while the sounds of a steel band filtered through the warm breeze. Then I was abruptly thrown out of my beach chair and back to reality. Dr. W. was holding my hips and pushing me from side to side. I looked at Mark and then to the technician.

"There must be a kink in the catheter," Dr. Wrong barked. The image of a car tire on our garden hose flashed in my mind's eye. Then the motion stopped and the dye came shooting through the tube, spilling over into a dark opening on the screen.

"All clear," he said, snapping off his rubber gloves. My instructions were to go home and straight into a hot bath. "The dye hardens like cement," Dr. W. called over his shoulder and he was gone as quickly as he had arrived.

"Rest here for a while until I get back with the X-rays," the technician said. Mark joined me on the table as I sipped a glass of water. The wax from the cup left a few white pieces on my lips; Mark gently wiped them away.

"I didn't expect it to be that uncomfortable," I said, trying to sound positive, now that it was over.

"You did an awesome job," he replied.

"How are you feeling?" The technician was back and she was holding my X-rays.

"I would like to get up," I replied.

"Let's go slow," she said while she handed me an X-ray of my Fallopian tubes.

I sat up with my legs draped over the side of the table. As I looked down at my legs swinging, the image of Edith Ann, Lily Tomlin's character, came floating into my mind. *And that's the truth, "ppths"* (the raspberry sound).

Mark and I rallied for position to see the X-ray, using the overhead fluorescent light. Our foreheads were nearly touching when I blurted out, "What's this?"

"Oh, that's just gas," the technician said. I giggled with embarrassment.

"Are you sure you didn't X-ray Mark? He is the one with the gas in our family."

"Thanks, dear," Mark shot back. The huge black spot on the X-ray was sitting close to what looked like a shoelace.

"What's this?" I asked.

"Your tube," the nurse replied.

At home, I followed doctor's orders and went straight into the bathtub. The water washed away the remnants of the procedure and the pain. I could hear Dr. W's voice.

"We'll go one step at a time, you only need to know about the next procedure, the next time I see you it will be for a post-coital. We'll rule out the simple things first and then move onto the more invasive procedures." What could be more invasive than having dye shot up into your tubes? I wondered.

"What is a post-coital?" I asked Mark from the bathtub.

"I don't know, we'll have to read about it, " he replied.

Girlfriend to Girlfriend:

During my journey I joined RESOLVE, the national non-profit organization that provides infertility education, advocacy and support for people experiencing infertility. At the time, I could not bring myself to attend any of their seminars or participate in other services they offered, but I devoured their newsletter. You can check for your local RESOLVE chapter on the web or call the National Office in Somerville, MA at 617-623-0744. You don't have to go through this journey alone!

9

Chapter Two
ART Will Make You Cry

To dry one's eyes and laugh at a fall,
And baffled, get up and begin again.
        Robert Browning (1812-1889)

"On the first day of Christmas my true love gave to me a partridge in a pear tree. On the second day of Christmas my true love gave to me sperm for a post-coital and a partridge in a pear tree." I was serenading Mark on our forty-five minute ride to Dr. Wrong's office.

He looked at me as I was doubled over in the front seat from laughter. At least I could amuse myself. Mark did not see the humor in my rendition of the Christmas classic.

I am a true believer in the spirit of Christmas and Santa Claus. There has to be some good in everything. I may be a little, OK a lot, of a Pollyanna. I consistently look for the open window when God shuts a door. He wouldn't just leave you hanging there, right? There has to be some divine order to things. But at this moment, I was having difficulties finding the message.

We parked our car and walked through the cement parking garage holding hands. The wind whistled as it whipped through the two open sides of the parking level. The cold breeze hurt my eyes as I moved in closer to Mark for protection.

"We'll start with the less-invasive procedures." Dr. Wrong's words were echoing in my head.

A post-coital exam is when you make love to your husband or partner and then drive to the doctor's office, strip naked from the waist down, and then allow him to insert another drink box straw into your vagina, up to your cervix, and collect the remnants of your lovemaking. It was so embarrassing. The naked part I could deal with, the doctor digging around in my privates I could escape with a mind vacation, but the fact that the whole office knew that Mark and I had just been intimate really bothered me. It's our sacred act. It was the consummation of

11

our love for each other and now here was this third party intruding on it. The thought of it made me dry heave.

I registered with nurse "Big Mouth" and she said, "We know what you've been up to, girlfriend." I flashed an annoyed smile and joined Mark in the row of waiting chairs. I could feel my skin beginning to turn red and blotchy.

"Let's just get this over with!" I whispered into Mark's ear. He had escaped into some outdated magazine.

Mark and I are both entrepreneurs and have this terrible habit of fixing other people's businesses. It's our game that we play. In a local restaurant, Mark will redesign the flow of the fast food line. It always begins with "You know what I would do if I owned this restaurant (dry cleaners, gas station…)?" "No, dear, what would you do?" is my standard response. The game was beginning to rub off on me.

"Mark, why do you suppose they use these terrible fluorescent overhead lights?" I was now lying on Dr. W.'s examination table, the blue polka-dotted johnny exposing my pale legs for the world to see. "They're blinding me. And you think they would put some nice artwork on the ceiling so that you could look at it while you're waiting." My husband was oblivious to my whining.

Dr. Wrong flew into the room in a whirlwind and announced in a deadpan fashion, "I got the results of your hystropinagram, you have a T-shaped uterus, it won't affect your getting pregnant, but it will increase your chances of a miscarriage." He once again moved closer into my open legs.

"What?" I replied. "A T-shaped uterus?"

He went on to say, "Your mother took DES while she was carrying you, correct?"

"Uh huh, I believe so," I mumbled.

"It's a side effect from that drug," he answered, seeming bored at having to deal with rookies like us. He was speaking while he was stretching my mucus, which looked like egg whites. He had the slide in his right hand and the protective slide cover in his left. He moved his hands up and down and my mucus formed a long transparent strand that reminded me of a spider web.

"Mucus is good," he announced. He then placed the slide under the microscope on the counter as he bent down to review it.

Mark's shadow danced on the wall as he shifted his weight from one leg to the other. It felt as though the energy in the room had been sucked out. It wasn't a good sign that Dr. W. had slowed his pace down and had been looking through the eyepiece for what seemed to be an eternity.

Coldly, Dr. Wrong announced that we should have five to ten live, moving sperm on this slide. Our slide held two. Two little guys. Two long-tailed big-headed sperm. Swimming effortlessly across the slide. Wiggling and gliding. The others... well, let's just say they were moving to a different drummer. There was the dog-chasing-the-tail sperm. The "hey-look-I-have-two-tails" sperm and the ones that were not alive.

I witnessed my husband's olive complexion turn pale. Dr. Wrong momentarily directed his attention towards Mark.

"You'll need to see an urologist and produce a sperm specimen." Then abruptly focusing on me, "The next test is an uterine scraping, it may cause minor discomfort."

"What's a uterine scraping?" I asked in a childlike tone.

"I'll go in and remove the endometrial lining to determine if your uterine lining can support a pregnancy."

"That sounds extremely painful!" I cracked back to Dr. Wrong.

"Minor discomfort, that's all."

"Have you ever had an uterine scraping?" I quickly replied. He looked at me and left the room obviously annoyed. He definitely missed the bedside manner class that should be required when dealing with such sensitive issues.

I had just witnessed my husband's manhood being violated. Nothing in life prepares you for this situation. I jumped off the examination table still clinging to the sheet covering my body; Mark was still bent over the slide.

"It will be OK, Mark, let me look," I whispered. My heart broke as I strained to hold the sheet and keep one eye closed while focusing with the other. We had rapidly descended into a place that we were not ready to enter.

13

Up until to this point the suspicion of who was the one with the reproductive challenges had always been me. I had no inkling that Mark might have issues. Dr. Wrong's checklist of tests had cleared me and the finger was now clearly pointed at Mark. My best friend, soul mate and lover.

The ride home was a slow motion blur. I wanted to get my husband home to the safety of our house.

"I'll support you through your test as you have for me, Mark. I'll go with you to give your sample."

"The sooner the better," Mark replied as he walked into our bedroom and shut the door.

ART's room

In ART's world, the room that gentlemen use to provide a sample has a nickname: *the spank tank*. It had to have been a man that started to refer to it in that manner.

Regardless of how it got its name, that's where we were headed. It was our next stop on the fun-filled, action packed adventures in infertility land.

The tank, the room. The thought of it made me giggle like some schoolgirl seeing her first penis. I felt mischievous and naughty at the same time.

We arrived at the hospital lab just in the nick of time. They stop accepting samples at 9:00 AM and it was 8:50 AM. We're so lucky!

The "tank" area reminded me of Monty Hall's show, *Let's Make a Deal*. Will it be door number one or door number two? "Carol, what's behind door number one?"

In our case, room A or room B. We chose room B; it was bigger and had more amenities. A TV and VCR, the pleather (you know the type, the fake leather chair made to look authentic) recliner, and its own bathroom area.

The female lab technician was old hat at the protocol of the tank. She rattled off the instructions as if she was giving directions to some lost tourist.

"Take this cup, don't touch the sides, write your name on the top, leave it on the counter. You haven't ejaculated immediately prior to producing the sample, have you?"

14

To any observer during this exchange, I looked like a normal supportive wife. On the inside I was laughing hysterically. Laughing at each instruction and running an internal dialogue– "Kristen, what the hell is wrong with you, you're here to support Mark, ha ha ha ha." Finally, there was no containing my immaturity. The laughter leaked out and had the effect of a fart in church. Mark shot me a look and I could not regain control. Mark was annoyed with me and he had every right to be.

My face began to hurt from laughing. I had to double over not to pee my undies. I cleared my throat, "May I go with my husband into room B? Is company permitted?"

"Yes," is all I heard and I resumed my party of one.

Why on earth Mark allowed me to follow him from the contained check-in area, across the shiny tiled floor, into room B is beyond me. I was already useless.

As he opened the wood door into the dimly light tan room I felt like a nervous hussy. I felt like I going where only "those kind of girls" would go. I was afraid and my hands were sweaty. We're married, for God's sake, and we had consummated our relationship. Why then was I feeling nervous? Maybe it was because Mark and I had never been intimate before in a room that had an "Occupied" light over its door.

The spank tank had a definite indescribable odor, like someone's nappy socks. I began sniffing in different directions to locate the origin of the culprit odor. Mark yelled, "Knock it off!" and I started into my second or it might have been my third giggling fit. The dark rug was stained and magazines looked worn. I was amazed that they really do offer tapes and magazines for use at discretion of the occupant.

My husband was a man with a mission. He began to take off his pants and fold them so they would lie over the pleather chair. He was naked from the waist down, now this was a change, and began his descent into the chair.

"Nooooo! Noo!" I yelled. "Do you know how many other naked from the waist down men have sat on this pleather chair?" He stopped mid-descent, his dark socks circling his Italian ankles and flashed a look that could have stopped a freight train. I reached over and began to hand him paper towels to sit on.

Ffwhp, ffwhp filled the air as I pulled another towel out of the dispenser.

"Forget it!" he growled.

The laughter bubble once again burst and I went into another laughing fit. This one caused a minor urine leakage into my underwear. "I have to use the toilet."

"What are you doing?!" Mark looked at me as I straddled the toilet bowl, hovering over the porcelain, trying not to touch the seat. The urine gushed into the bowl. "You have to leave," Mark demanded.

I realized that I was using my sense of humor to get through this ordeal. I was better equipped to handle my procedures than to support Mark through his. "I'm so sorry, honey." I began to apologize to my husband for my juvenile behavior. I was there to support him during his time of need, as he had been there for me, but I dropped the ball, so to speak. In this case it would have been better for Mark to handle "his" alone.

I zipped up my pants and stood next to Mark. He proceeded to handle this task solo and we exited room B with a clean catch of a specimen, labeled correctly, and placed perfectly timed on the counter of the nurses' desk. I'm positive they heard us in our attempt to complete this mission. I sure they were thinking, "What the hell are those two doing?" I didn't care. I would never see them again. To me it was yet another job well done!

All there was left for us to do was to wait. Wait for the fate of my husband's manhood to be recorded and reviewed by the medical establishment. Wait to see if there was something seriously wrong with Mark. What if it was a tumor or cancer? The emotional Kristen immediately leapt to the worst case scenario, rushing past all logical reasons for a low sperm count to a place of sheer and utter lack of rational thinking, low sperm count equals cancer.

I began to pray. "Please take this cup away from my husband. Oh God, our Father, please send us the strength to get through this ordeal. Can you hear me, God?"

I then decided that the post-coital test was just a bad sperm day for Mark. That it was the way the drink box straw was inserted into my vagina that produced the poor results. Dr.

Wrong just must have missed the good grouping of my husband's "he-man" sperm. I was slipping into my coping mechanism, denial. But there was no denying my fears that something could be seriously wrong with Mark.

We worked elbow-to-elbow in our home office all day on the 23rd of December. The weather was cold and gray, which was very appropriate for the feeling in our home. I was wondering if my presence made passing the time worse for Mark. We both were putting on brave fronts. Each time the phone rang, we jumped and darted for it. For me, it was a form of torture waiting to hear the results.

Mark left for a late appointment and we arranged to be in constant communication in case I received a call from Dr. Wrong. I believe that fate has a way of working things out the way they should be; there had to be a reason that Mark left our house and then the call came. I was home alone preparing dinner when I answered the phone.

"Kristen, this is Dr. Wrong." There was no exchange of pleasantries, just right into the test results. "All your tests are fine, Kristen, your hormone levels are within normal limits. Mark, on the other hand, did not fare as well. The count was very low but most disconcerting was that the motility and morphology was poor."

"What does this mean?" My voice cracked.

"This means the sperm were not formed correctly and they are not motile." I translated this into they were deformed and could not swim. "Mark needs to see an urologist and I'll see you next month for the uterine scraping."

"Thank you for calling," I whispered as I hung up the receiver. Why was I thanking him?

I was not equipped to break this news to my husband. I began to pace around our kitchen island; with each lap came a new version of the dialogue until my practice session was ended with the ring of the phone.

"Hi, my love." Mark's voice was warm and strong on the other end of the line. "Did he call?"

I answered with a quick, "Yes."

"What did he say?"

17

"I'll tell you when you get home."   The image of my husband, seat-belted into our overturned car flashed in my mind's eye, while I thought, this news is enough to make anyone drive off the road.

"No, tell me now," Mark said.

"Where are you? I'll wait for you to come home."

Mark's voice got stern. "Kristen, tell me now!"

No, I thought, not when you're in the car and I can't be there to wrap my arms around you and hold you.   "Well, it's not what we hoped," I said.

"What did he say, Kristen?"

"It's low."

I felt the knife go into my husband's chest and I was the one pushing it. Goddamn! Why are we in this situation? God, what are you thinking? I'm hurting the person I would lay down my life for! And why, God? Where the hell are you?

Mark interrupted my argument with God.

"Kristen!" he barked. "What else did he say?"

"We'll discuss it when you get home."

"What else did he say, Kristen?" He knew me well enough to know I was holding back. Holding back the worst of the news, if anything could get worse.

"The motility and morphology is not good. You really need to see the urologist." You could have cut the silence with the knife that I just pushed into his chest.

"What are the numbers?" We had been reading about the normal range test scores and focused on the number we wanted as an outcome. Our numbers were far from the desired test results.

Twenty minutes later, the sound of our garage door opening made me jump and I rushed to greet Mark as he entered through the kitchen. He was all business.

"Where are your notes? What did he actually say? What does this mean?"

"Per million," I replied.

"Couldn't have you taken better notes? What is this word?"

18

"Mobility." I felt as though there should have been a white light shining in my eyes. Then we both became silent and I began to cry. "I'm sorry, Mark, I'm so sorry."

We held each other and began to move slowly to the music that was playing. As an early Christmas gift, Mark had just purchased John Denver's *Greatest Hits* for me. The song "You Fill up My Senses" filled our family room. It paced our mood as our emotions broke down. We both sobbed. It was the release of all the pressure and anticipation of the past. We cried for our present situation, the past lost opportunities to create our family and we mourned our uncertain future.

Where are you, God?

Girlfriend to Girlfriend: Think Abundance

When my glue started to come undone, I called a friend of mine who is a family therapist to discuss my attitude around our fertility challenges. As always his words were direct and cut to the chase.

"Kristen, you're in a scarcity mentality; I didn't once hear you refer to any of the abundance in your life, you're just focusing on what you don't have!"

I responded with a long pause and then "Yah?"

Believe me, I know how truly difficult this suggestion is but here goes. Try daily to recognize the abundance in your day – the sunshine, clean sheets, a warm cup of tea, a scented candle, anything and everything. I'll talk more about this at the end of the next chapter, but it really did help. So, my friend, try to "Think Abundance."

Also, schedule ten minutes a day just to think about your situation. I started doing this after a conversation with my "think abundance" friend. I was totally distracted during the day with our childlessness and daily living, work and everything else, was suffering. So, during the day if a thought would come and I started to concentrate on it, I would simply jot the thought down on a sticky note and save it for later. It saved my sanity. Some days I needed more than 10 minutes and others it was less. But this strategy gave me permission to feel what I needed to feel

19

and also gave me the concentration I needed for living my daily life.

Chapter Three
Mark Becomes a Connoisseur of ART

In adversity, remember to keep an even mind.
    Horace (65-8 B.C.)

The warmth of the fireplace radiated throughout the living room as the twinkling Christmas lights added to the glow. The entire room ducked as the first wad of wrapping paper was projected across the room–Uncle Tom was the recipient of a wrapping paper ball by Uncle Frank. My uncles, my mother's brothers and brother-in-law, had just begun the ritual of throwing the crumpled-up Christmas wrapping paper at anyone and everyone and I noticed Mark retreat into the family room. I quickly followed.

"Are they getting to be too much?" I asked.

"No, I just need some time alone," Mark replied.

We were with my family, celebrating the Christmas holiday, and at times the family as a whole can be overwhelmingly loud. It was difficult to get annoyed with the group, though, because they enjoyed each other's company so much.

I felt that physically I was in the comfort of my family, the laughter and love was there, but emotionally I was absent. Mark and I were bearing the burden of our "secret" together. I sat down beside Mark in my sister's family room and began to fiddle with my Christmas gift from him. He truly amazed me. In the midst of this crisis, he was still considerate and thoughtful.

When we had been in Canada on a business trip together, I had admired a tri-gold rolling wedding ring we saw in a store. It was very plain and simple. It was also quite expensive. I had lusted over it.

On Christmas morning we had exchanged gifts. Mark handed me a box the size of a shoebox. Sure enough, it was slippers... fuzzy boa high-heeled slippers, the kind of slippers a woman of grand leisure would wear.

What the hell is he thinking! I thought when I opened them. "Oh, how nice, honey, thank you so much!"

21

I quickly placed them on the floor. On Mark's insistence, I tried them on. Placing the right slipper on the floor, I began to jam my foot into the green boa-covered toe.

"I can't seem to get my foot in, there's something in the toe." I stuck my hand into the slipper and hit something hard.

I pulled out what I thought was packing material and it was a beautiful red box with a gold design on the top and side. I slowly opened the box and screeched. Mark placed the ring we had seen on my finger and we kissed like we were lovers.

That was this morning, at home. Now, the silence in the room and between us was a stark contrast to the rumpus happening a few feet away. As a wad of wrapping paper skidded into the room, my mind wandered back to the telephone conversation with Dr. Wrong about Mark's physical condition. I had immediately imagined the worst. I looked at Mark.

"What?" he asked.

"Nothing," I replied. How could I share with him the fact that I was fearing that the worst might be happening– cancer.

Believing that thoughts are things and can create what tomorrow's reality might hold, I willed the negative thoughts away and began to concentrate on solving this situation.

I decided to begin my quest for an urologist. Mentally, I was forming my game plan. When I get home tomorrow, I'll call the urologist's office that Dr. Wrong referred, and tell them that three months is way too long to wait; we won't wait three months! As a matter of fact, I'll call them daily until they take us sooner. I'll pester them until they take us. And if that fails, I'll begin to whine.

Where is the open window, God?

The day after Christmas, my first call was to the referred urologist. The receptionist recognized my voice.

"Mrs. Magnacca, we told you that we are all booked for the next three months and yes, we have put you on the cancellation list."

"I don't think you understand our circumstances, I need my husband to be seen today."

"As I told you before, you were given our first available appointment."

I hung up the receiver, sticking out my tongue. To hell with you!

Now I was pissed.

"This is Kristen Magnacca. I need to speak with Dr. Wrong immediately."

"He's with a patient."

"Interrupt him!" I was so forceful I scared myself.

"What can I do for you, Kristen?" Dr. Wrong bellowed with impatience.

"I need another urologist: the doctor you gave us has a three-month wait. I want Mark seen immediately."

"There is another doctor in Wellesley, I'm not sure of the number. It's Wellesley Urologist or something. Have a good day." The conversation ended.

I hit the flash button with my index finger and quickly dialed 411.

"I need the number for Wellesley Urology in Wellesley, MA," I cried. The operator's voice was calm.

"I have a listing for Dr. L. under urologist but no Wellesley Urology."

"I'll take it!"

My index finger hit flash again. I was in full-blown fight-or-flight mode when a pleasant voice answered on the second ring.

"Dr. L.'s office, how may I help you?"

"My name is Kristen Magnacca, I'm calling on behalf of my husband Mark, it is imperative that he is seen as soon as possible by Dr. L., you see, I fear there may be something terribly wrong." As the words left my lips, I broke down. I was sobbing into the phone. The women's demeanor was soft and comforting.

"OK, Mrs. Magnacca, let's see what I can do... we'll see you on Wednesday at 1:00 P.M., how's that?"

"Do you mean this Wednesday, as in two days from now?"

"Yes, does that work with your schedule?"

"Yes, yes, thank you so much, thank you so much." I sniffled and wiped my nose.

23

The breeze blew in from God's open window!

Dr. L's office was located in the medical building adjacent to the hospital. Upon entering the office it was apparent that we were the youngest people in the waiting area. This office was in total contrast to Dr. Wrong's office. It had a fish tank, cherry mahogany furniture, clean carpets and a well-stocked supply of up-to-date magazines. The office screamed, "We care."

The older people in the office reviewed us, trying to determine our reason for being there, but this time the receptionist greeted us as people and whispered quietly that we should fill out the form and Dr. L would be right with us.

I noticed a younger, red haired doctor pass by the waiting room and my curiosity was piqued. Was that him? God, he looked young. This redhead of a doctor actually came into the waiting room and acknowledged an elderly woman's husband. His pleasant voice filled the room.

"She's 100 percent again, she did a great job recovering from surgery." The husband beamed back and I instantly knew that he had been the one nursing her back to her feet.

Then the doctor spun around and introduced himself to Mark and me.

"Hi, I'm Dr. L. I'll be right with you after I'm finished with this young lady." Pinch me I must be dreaming.

Dr. L took us back to his office. The cherry mahogany decor was throughout the office. His office was clear of any clutter and his desktop was organized with no distractions. Our file was the only piece of paper taking up real estate on his desktop. The shine from his desk was almost blinding.

"What brings you to see me today?" Dr. L. began. In stereo, both of us started to speak at once. I deferred the storytelling to Mark, who told our tale while Dr. L. listened attentively. He shut our file and leaned across his desk, carefully choosing his words.

"My wife is a DES daughter; it took a little longer than what is considered normal and then we had our son." He passed his son's picture across his desk while sharing this intimate detail.

My mouth dropped open. His words and act of comfort came at the most needed time.

"Well, let's take a look, Mark, then we can see what we're dealing with." He then stood and asked Mark to follow him into his examining room. "It will take a moment and then we'll return."

I stood also, turning to leave my coat on my chair. In an instant, Mark spun around. "Stay here, Kristen."

"Oh yeah," I said and slowly lowered myself back into my seat.

I had lost my right to attend any inner circle appointment with Mark because of my behavior in the spank tank. The thought of me bent over laughing and urinating in my underwear brought a smile to my face and an audible laugh. Who could argue with Mark?

I could hear his muffled voice behind me and then both men laughing. I was only seated for what seemed to be two minutes before Dr. L. and Mark were back in their previous spots.

"It's a varicocele, a varicose vein in the scrotum area. It's fixable with surgery," Dr. L. informed us.

"Thank God."

"The enlarged blood vessel carries extra blood to the area, turning the heat up in the kitchen, so to speak. And when the heat is up, the count goes down and so does the ability to swim and the sperm's shape."

Mark would need surgery. Dr. L. began describing the process.

"It's a simple procedure. I will make an incision into the abdomen and cut the blood vessel, reducing the blood flow to the area." This is how my internal translator related the process to my layman's ears. "You can schedule it now if you like, on your way out of the office just stop and see Martha."

Mark has an experiential metaprogram, which means he has to ask, read, and do what he feels necessary before entering into the unknown. The days following our visit to Dr. L. were filled with us reading about this condition, statistics of before and after surgery experiences, complications, and success rates. Dr. L.

requested another sperm test (this time Mark flying solo!) and blood test to ensure their accuracy.

Mark was immersed in the process of educating himself as to what was about to happen. At night I would hear the computer modem beep as it gained access to the Web. I knew that Mark was in Yahoo searching for information. He discovered a new procedure and faxed it over to Dr. L.

After this discovery, we made an unannounced visit to Dr. L.

"Mark and Kristen, come on back to my office."

We took the same seats that we had only a week prior. Dr. L. pulled a book off his shelf and showed Mark the procedure in color pictures. He seemed to know exactly how to deal with Mark; it must be a man's thing. Then he shared with us that he also had had the same condition and had undergone the surgery that Mark would be having. It wove a common bond between them, patient and doctor.

"Mark, take a stool softener after your surgery. I didn't and really wished I had when trying to have my first bowel movement," Dr. L whispered. Who would have thought? This helpful hint made the difference in his "bathroom" recovery.

On its second day of operation we entered the brand-new surgical wing, at O'darkthirty in the morning. As the automatic doors opened, the smell of newness greeted us.

"Look, Mark, a rainbow, that has to be a good omen." The bright morning's sunbeams were creating a rainbow on the shiny new tile floor that spanned throughout the entryway. Following instructions, we checked in at the desk and were escorted to the pre-surgical area. The cool green and light tan combination was soft and comforting as Mark began to get settled in his room.

"Hi, I'm Charlotte and I'll be your nurse today. I'll need you to use the men's room and then change into the hospital best." She handed Mark a polka-dotted sky-blue johnny, a blue robe, and paper slippers. Mark turned and followed Charlotte into the little boy's room.

He returned in his hospital attire, holding his bathrobe shut and fluffing his pillow at the same time as he boarded his gurney. If it weren't for his facial hair I would have thought he was about twelve. He looked so childlike.

26

"Hey hon, can I have my Walkman?" Mark asked.

We are so alike and yet so different. Mark is a "stuff" person. On vacation I use one bag and he uses two cars to haul all his vacation accessories.

"Ouch!" I cried as I nearly pulled my back out picking up his knapsack. "What do you have in here?"

"Not now, Kristen."

I began to wade through the contents of his knapsack after placing it on the gurney. Three books.

"When did you think you were going to read these?"

"You don't know how long these things take."

His dayrunner.

"Planning to work today?"

"OK, OK, Kristen." Three granola bars. "For later," Mark piped. An apple and banana. "I might be hungry later." A change of clothes. "Just in case." Then finally, on the bottom, his Walkman.

During our operation preparation time, Mark had created a positive affirmation tape to be played during his surgery. He painstakingly picked the music he wanted to listen to while unconscious and interspersed his own voice saying, "You'll begin to heal as soon as the surgery begins, all is well." We are strong believers in the mind/body connection, plus making this tape gave Mark something to do to take his mind off the upcoming surgery. It would be a long process, so the music he chose was very relaxing.

Mark immediately plugged himself into his tape. The nurse arrived to double-check the IV dripping into Mark's left arm.

Charlotte noticed his gold wedding ring.

"You'll have to take that off now, Mark," she said pointing to his finger.

"What?"

I reached over and lifted one of the headphones off his ear. "She would like you to remove your wedding ring, honey," I said slowly.

"This ring hasn't left my finger since the day my wife put it on. I prefer to leave it right where it is." I was surprised at Mark.

27

Charlotte reached into her pocket and pulled out some white surgical tape.

"I'll just tape it to your finger, OK? You don't have to remove it." Mark leaned back into his pillow and closed his eyes. Charlotte then walked behind Mark and put a blue shower cap on his head. "Any time now, the nurse will be in to give him his 'cocktail.'"

I nodded and began to cry, but quickly wiped my eyes and looked up.

"Please, God and all Mark's angels and guides be with him as he undergoes this surgery, send your white healing light. Amen." I managed to push the thoughts of Mark having any difficulties during the procedure out of my mind.

His surgical nurse returned and injected a drug into his IV. "You'll begin to feel sleepy now, Mark." The nurse spoke quietly.

"OK," he responded with his eyes closed and pulled the headphones over his ears again.

Dr. L. arrived to collect Mark. "Hey, Mark, I read the book last night and I think I'm ready."

I laughed. I guess the drugs were taking effect because Mark did not get the fact that Dr. L. was yanking his chain.

I quickly got out of my chair and out of the way as the surgical staff surrounded the bed.

"You can say your good-byes." Charlotte stopped the bed. I leaned over Mark; his brown eyes looked into mine.

"I love you so much, thank you for doing this." My eyes began to tear.

"I love you too."

"I'll be waiting right here, OK?"

I watched as the back of Mark's head bopped to the music on his Walkman. His feet were moving back and forth to the same rhythm. Grinning and shaking my head I said quietly, "God, he's in your hands now!"

I quickly reached into my pocket for my beeper to make sure it was on. What a great idea–upon registration the receptionist had asked me, "Would you like a beeper, Mrs. Magnacca?"

"A beeper?"

She went on to explain, "That way Dr. L. will page you immediately after the surgery and you can pick up any hospital telephone and dial the number shown. The pagers only work on the hospital grounds, though." I took the pager and clipped it onto my pocketbook.

"Thank you."

I took a seat in the foyer of the hospital. Placing Mark's knapsack on the chair next to me, I leaned back and closed my eyes as the sun's rays warmed my face. I sent Mark loving, healing energy and prayed that all would go well.

The surgery took longer than I anticipated. I began to worry and think to myself, I hope he's OK, he's fine, Kristen, stop thinking that way, why is it taking so long, though? He's fine. My mental game of tennis continued until I could not stand the waiting anymore. I got up and walked over to the receptionist. Then I heard my beeper. Thank God, it's over.

I quickly dialed 3570.

"Dr. L., how may I help you?" Just hearing the doctor's voice put me at ease.

"This is Kristen Magnacca."

"Kristen, he's fine, the operation went well, we'll have to wait about three months before we see the improvement, but Mark's fine. I'll send someone to get you when he leaves recovery."

"You're awesome, thank you, doctor."

I returned to my seat for a millisecond and then began to pace the floor. I wanted to be upstairs now, to see Mark with my own eyes and know that he was fine. I heard someone calling my name, or, rather, trying to say our name. "That's me."

"I'll take you to Mark now, he's sitting up and drinking some ginger ale."

As I came around the curtain I recognized Mark's feet. He was disoriented and sitting in his little blue robe with a terrible case of bedhead, eating graham crackers and sipping ginger ale. "Hey!" he shouted. I realized he was still groggy and was actually surprised I was there. "Can I have a granola bar?" The second thing out of his mouth was about food, so I knew he was fine.

I was so in love with my husband. I teared up again. "I love you Mark." I kissed his bedhead.

"I love you, too."

We left the hospital with a bottle of Percocets for the pain and our agenda in mind: create our family.

Kristen becomes a connoisseur of ART

Prior to losing some of my sense, when the logical twin was still in command, I had made an appointment with a reproductive endocrinologist referred to me by my midwife. He had had a three month wait, which I felt at the time was too far off and a colossal waste of prime baby-making time, so I went down the Dr. Wrong road.

While Mark was recovering from his surgery, I decided that Dr. Wrong and I were not a match and canceled the uterine scraping. I just could not bring myself to have my uterus scraped–just the phrase caused me great distress.

Reviewing my dayrunner, I noticed the Dr. Right appointment starred in the calendar block. Why not wait to see this doctor instead? My pencil tapping on the wooden desk mimicked my biological clock ticking. Look what we have already experienced in the ninety days it took to get this appointment.

"Mark, will you be able to come?"

"I wouldn't miss it," he replied with a smile.

My Dr. Right was located in my midwife's office, so for me it was like old home week. I considered the nurses there my newly-found friends and Mark and I were greeted warmly.

Dr. Right was tall and handsome, with sandy brown hair. He wore a lab coat with his name embroidered over the left pocket: Dr. Right, M.D, Ph.D., reproductive endocrinologist. He almost needed another side of his chest to fit all his credentials.

I felt an immediate "like" with him. He spoke in a soft, respectful manner. His words melted my fears and apprehension away like a cool waterfall running over moss covered rocks.

"Mark and I have had some procedures done and I canceled the uterine scraping because I did not feel I could handle that procedure at this time."

Dr. R was quick with his response. "A uterine scraping is a barbaric test. The same results can be obtained through a vaginal ultrasound."

"Thank God I trusted my instincts. It just didn't feel right," I said.

"Do you think you could handle an ultrasound? It would be done two doors down."

"Sure!" jumped out of my mouth.

"Let's schedule a follow-up consultation after the ultrasound and, Mark, it might be good to have another semen analysis," Dr. R. said. Dr. Right concluded our initial meeting with a pelvic exam. This time Mark knew with certainty his spot to stand in. I was dressed in the appropriate attire, the blue polka-dotted johnny and was in "the position."

"Come in," I answered the quiet knock on the door. Dr. R. came in and washed his hands and left the water running. What is he doing? I thought.

Picking up the speculum he ran it under the warm water, then he inserted it into my vagina. Oh, my God, this is the first time in my life a doctor has ever done this for me. I really LIKE him! I wasn't sure if I said that out loud or internally.

The exam was respectfully completed and then Dr. R. said, "I'll see you soon, it was nice meeting you both." After shaking Mark's hand, he turned with a smile and left.

"Mark, I think I love him," I gushed.

"OK, I know, let's get you dressed."

"No, no, Mark, I really think I love him!" I was half-kidding and half-serious.

"Yah, yah, let's go, I'm hungry."

"What else is new!"

I felt an excitement again that I hadn't had in a long time. I felt that we were in the correct place for us. I knew we would work out the problem areas and have a child, I just knew it. How could we not with all the letters after Dr. R.'s name?

The day of my ultrasound appointment, I was already beginning to think our car could get us back to the doctor's office on autopilot. I felt comfortable entering into the office with its pale pink furniture and soft muted green floral couch. I walked across the carpet to register with the receptionist as Mark followed.

"They're ready for you now, Kristen, come on around." Denise greeted me on the other side of the glass partition. "Do you have to use the ladies' room?"

"Doesn't she always?" Mark chimed in from behind me.

I urinated and followed Denise into the ultrasound room. The lights were off and the room was still, the hum of the ultrasound machine reminding me of the computers in our office. "You're dressed perfect for today."

I was wearing a long dress with no panty hose, just sandals. I was able to remove my undies, pull up my dress and get right onto the table without undressing.

Girlfriend to Girlfriend:
I saved valuable time during my infertility vaginal ultrasounds by wearing my "uniform" of a long dress and knee highs, if of course the weather permitted. No need for a johnny or to disrobe. Just a lap cover and we were off to the races.

To my right there was a table with a TV on it. There was a keyboard with what looked like vertical light-dimming switches. Mark came and stood on my left and reached for my hand.

Denise reached down and discreetly put some KY jelly on the condom-covered ultrasound wand. My heart skipped a beat when I saw the size of that wand.

"You're going to feel my fingers and then I'll insert the probe," Denise said. She handled that equipment as if she was driving a shift stick. Drop down to first, this is your uterus, shifting into second, your cervix coming up, and then the engine stalled when we were about to go into third, my ovaries and tubes.

At that point, the energy changed dramatically in the room. I knew in an instant something was wrong. She immediately stopped the flow of information; it seemed our tour car had run out of gas. Denise was still moving the vaginal wand and sliding the light dimmer switch up and down but not saying a word.

"What are you looking at now?"

"I'm checking the thickness of your uterus."

"What's that?" I asked.

"Kristen, Dr. R. will review this with you at your appointment." Something was wrong. I knew it.

"OK, all set, you can get cleaned up and Dr. R. will discuss your results," Denise said with a smile.

The KY jelly had left me with a sticky mess. Wiping myself and slipping into my undies I said, "Mark, do you think something is wrong?"

"No, Kristen, I think it's not her job to tell us in-depth information."

"Are you sure?"

"Yes!" With a kiss, Mark opened the door to leave. I took my first step out of the room and felt strangeness to the energy in the hallway; all the nurses and other technicians stopped and looked my way, a look of knowing something I didn't. I shrugged off the stares, smiled and walked past. I dismissed the scenario as paranoia and drove home with Mark.

Tell me it isn't so, ART

Standing naked in front of my closet, experiencing major clothes anxiety, I pulled out my short sleeved black dress. It was perfect. It added a romantic element to my meeting Dr. R. for our consultation regarding Mark's latest trip to the spank tank and my ultrasound. I giggled out loud. "Hey, Mark, do you think Dr. R. will like this dress?"

Mark just rolled his eyes and walked away, mumbling, "*I* like the dress."

"Well, you know that I love him!"

"Oh boy." This game had taken on a life of its own.

The little black summer dress made me feel good, pretty, and maybe even a little sexy, something that I hadn't felt in a while. My reproductive organs were for one purpose and one purpose only – a child. The thought of actually seducing my husband and enjoying the act of lovemaking was almost foreign to me.

As we were escorted back to Dr. Right's office I enjoyed how the dress moved and how it felt rubbing up against my bare legs. The New England winter had been so long and the weather report of sun and temperatures in the high seventies made for a treat for mid-May.

We were seated in Dr. R's office. His smile was easy and he seemed in a hurry to get down to business.

"Mark, I have the results of your semen analysis... let's see, the chart indicated that you initially produced 15.2 million live sperm per cc when there should have been 60-150 million. The morphology had 23 percent categorized as mature, normal sperm."

I could feel the excitement in his voice as he continued. "Mark, there has been great improvement in your sperm count. There was a dramatic change for the better."

Mark slid to the edge of his seat. "Really?"

Dr. Right continued, passing Mark's chart across the desk. "Mark, your count has risen to 60 million, well within the normal range. Let's keep in mind that it has only been two months since your surgery, and that in another month or so, the numbers will probably be even higher."

My jaw dropped open and Mark stared at the chart while we both absorbed this awesome news.

"Sixty million? Wow! Sixty million? Thank you, God! And you think that there will be more improvement?" Mark was babbling.

It was apparent that Dr. Right was sharing in our euphoria.

"Sixty million, oh my God, Kristen, sixty million!" Mark must have repeated the numbers about 50 times.

My face was beginning to hurt from smiling. "I can't believe it, you're so wonderful, you go, Mark!" It was like a locker room celebration, high fives and all.

Dr. R. abruptly swiveled in his chair, positioned directly in front of me, a serious look washing over his face. Still celebrating our fertility challenge victory, I ignored his affect. I was waiting to hear the doctor's orders: "Go home, pretend you're a rabbit, and don't come out of your bedroom until you can't walk!"

The silence between us made me realize that what was coming was not good.

He spoke softly and with great compassion, which was in stark contrast to how he delivered Mark's news.

"The ultrasound revealed a problem, Kristen." I felt as though the wingback chair was engulfing me as I began to sink into it. "You do not have a T-shaped uterus."

"Well, that's good!" All the anguish I had put my mother through was for nothing; she had taken responsibility for my inability to conceive. My inner voice took on a nasty tone. Dr. Wrong is such an ASS.

Well, so far so good, I thought. The wingback chair was releasing me from its grip. Dr. Right cleared his throat and pulled out my ultrasound.

"See this dark area on the ultrasound?" he asked.

"Yes," I answered weakly.

"The dark spot on the ultrasound indicates something fluid-filled. This area is dangerously close to your tubes. Without going in for a look we won't know what the mass is or if it is impeding the functioning of your tube."

"Dark mass, what is it?" I asked fighting back my tears. "A tumor? Could it be cancer?" I continued after catching my breath.

"It is probably a cyst, Kristen, but what concerns me is the size," Dr. Right continued. "The surgery would be laproscopic, I would make a little incision into your belly button and two more down by your pubic area and then go in with a little camera and take a look. Or you could continue with an IUI, intrauterine insemination, if you prefer."

I glanced over to Mark for support and guidance. To my extreme annoyance he was still looking at his chart with his numbers.

"Can you believe this improvement?" he actually had the gall to utter. It was as though he lost his sense of hearing as soon as he learned his sperm count improved. All of a sudden he had "he man" sperm! His sammys can swim but now he'll need

35

a hearing aid or an ice pack for the black eye I was about to give him. Finally, I shot Mark the look. You know, the look a wife gives her husband, the "are you a total ass" look.

Dr. Right continued with my options. As my mind raced, the reality sunk in that the big mass on the X-ray from Dr. Wrong's office was not gas as the technician had indicated but was the same mass that Dr. R. had recognized as a possible cyst or something else. My internal dialogue turned ugly. What a jerk I was. Dr. W. didn't know his ass from his elbow. I allowed myself to go through so much already with that quack! Why didn't I wait to see Dr. R.? I lost all my sense, what a colossal waste of time, I'm going to call him and give him a piece of my mind!

Sinking deeper into the wingback chair, I gripped the arms of the chair with all my might. Snap out of it Kristen, FOCUS!

"Would you please repeat that?" I asked.

"Kristen, you don't have to make your mind up right now, you can go home and think about it."

"No, no, I need to make my mind up now." I knew that if I waited it would be more difficult for me.

Let's Make a Deal began to play in my head. "I'll take door Number One, Monty."

"OK, let's show Kristen what she's won!"

"No, I'll take door Number Two... oh, oh Monty, I'll take the money..."

"I'll go ahead with the insemination." I didn't want the surgery, I wanted a child.

Dr. R. quietly said, "That's fine, Kristen, but there is no way of knowing if your tubes are functional."

I sat for a moment as both men stared at me awaiting my response. I felt outnumbered. "I'll have the surgery," I barked.

Reaching for the phone, "I'll check the dates available now and schedule it for you." Dr. Right was pleased at my decision. I could tell that he wanted me to have the surgery but was allowing me to come to my own decision.

"No," I yelled, "I'll go for the insemination."

"OK."

"No, the surgery." I was so confused.

All of a sudden, my husband became the head male cheerleader for the surgical unit at our hospital. "Kristen, go and have the surgery. It's not a big deal. I already had an experience there! We know the routine. It will be OK." Boy, for a guy who manhandled everything and everyone about his surgery, he was sure throwing caution to the wind when I would be under the knife.

I leaned my head to the right and nestled it into the corner of the chair. I relaxed and let go and sat for a moment. Logic took over. If you go ahead with the IUI, Kristen, there is no way of knowing if Mark's "he man" sperm can get to the eggs. I'll be wasting time if my tubes are blocked. Mark went through his surgery and is OK. Look at his success. He's still gloating, for God's sake.

"I'll have the surgery," I said with certainty.

Dr. R. picked up the phone and scheduled my surgery. He swung around in his chair with the date. May 23rd.

"MAY 23RD! THAT'S MY BIRTHDAY!" I yelled.

"We can reschedule, Kristen, but it will be in July."

"That will be a three month wait, no, I'll take May 23rd."

Girlfriend to Girlfriend:

Start a journal. Prior to entering "Fertility Land" I was an avid journaler but then in the mist of our circumstances I stopped because I didn't like what I was reading from the previous day.

After the "Think Abundance" advice my friend gave me, I changed my approach to journaling. I would write down in list form at least five things per day that I was thankful for. Don't get me wrong– some days I had to concentrate and it was a stretch to come up with the five, but I did. Then I would let out all the emotions of the day and it helped. I strongly recommend starting with the five good things because after my written "emotional purging," I wasn't in the state of mind for anything positive.

37

Chapter Four
There Is No Denying ART

"Hope" is the thing with feathers–
That perches in the soul–
And sings the tune without the words–
And never stops–at all–
    Emily Dickinson (1830-1886)

I was comfortably numb, dealing with today and with what I was about to experience in a zombie-like state, hovering over my body, totally disengaged with my mind, body, and feelings. I was going through the motions but feeling nothing.

Unlike Mark, there was no pre-surgical preparation for me. I scheduled the surgery for my birthday and then pretended it did not exist until that morning. My denial strategy kicked in again.

My birthday morning, the doorbell rang and I scurried down the stairs to greet my mother, sister, and niece.

"Happy birthday Cocci, (the Polish word for aunt)" my niece Abigail sang when I opened the door. "We brought you a new dress for your birthday!"

"Abby, you're not supposed to tell," my sister ordered.

It was surreal. I was showered and dressed in my sweatpants and sweatshirt waiting to drive to the hospital for my surgery, and turning 34 simultaneously. My sister, a surgical nurse, wanted to come and speak with Dr. R. prior to the surgery. The plan was that my mother would stay at my house with Abigail, pacing most likely, and Mark would have my sister's company at the hospital. I just wanted to get this over with. To clear the way and be "normal."

We arrived at the hospital and followed the same procedure we had a few months earlier with Mark's surgery. Mark was correct; having his experience as a frame of reference did help. I knew what was about to happen to some extent.

This time it was me who followed the nurse to the little girl's room, returning in the same outfit that Mark had worn, and it was me holding my bathrobe shut as I mounted the hospital bed.

I noticed my ring finger on my left hand. It looked so bare.

"Hey, Mom, I'm leaving my jewelry and wedding ring on my dresser," I had yelled down to my mother in my kitchen. I had decided that I would leave all my jewelry at home, including my wedding ring. I just felt it would be safer.

I also left my styled hair and makeup there too. Catching a glimpse of myself in the mirror next to the bed, I was startled at how scary I looked.

"It must be the lights, next year you'll be able to dress up and go out for your birthday," I reassured myself.

The pre-surgical areas were made up of three nicely wallpapered walls and a curtained front. Our curtain pushed open and in walked Dr. R.

"Already had your cocktail, Kristen?" he asked.

"No, I just don't have any makeup on!"

He laughed. "Well, unfortunately we were bumped from our original scheduled time and your surgery will be delayed an hour and a half. We are in a holding pattern, are you OK with that?"

"I think so," sighing and then instantly beginning my internal dialogue. A hour and a half more, I'm not going to make it. I think I've changed my mind.

"I have to pee!" jumping out of the bed, dragging my IV. For the next hour and a half I urinated about twelve times. It must have been nerves because I wasn't allowed to eat or drink anything for 24 hours prior or maybe it was the chilly IV solution that was dripping into my arm.

Then my surgical team arrived. It was exactly as it had been for Mark.

"Any time now, Kristen, I'm going to give you the 'cocktail' and you'll begin to feel drowsy." It was the familiar voice of my nurse Charlotte whispering.

Instantly, I could not feel my nose. It had disappeared. Lifting my hand to my face, feeling for my nose, my hand moved in slow motion. I was so curious as to how this was happening that I wanted to watch my hand try to move again. I was focusing on my hand when the nurse, the anesthesiologist, and the rest of the surgical team began to move my bed.

Looking up, I saw Mark's dark eyes staring into mine.

"You'll be fine, I'm right here, I love you, Kristen." His lips pressed into mine. I could see his face next to mine but had no feeling. I was totally enthralled in this sensation when we entered the operating room.

I was half-drugged but very curious about what the room was like and how an operating room was set up.

It was tiled light green and it actually reminded me of the operating rooms that I've seen on television programs. It had large lights that looked like an alien space ship had landed on one side. The equipment was covered with the same hairnet, shower cap type material. The room looked cold and clean at the same time.

My gurney came to a stop next to the operating table.

"One, two, three!" I was lifted onto the table by the team. Then Dr. R. walked around the operating table and came to stand on my right side and hold my hand. As my thumb rubbed tiny circles into the back of his skilled hands, I lost the battle of staying on this plane and drifted off into the unknown darkness.

"Kristen, Kristen." His voice and my name were pulling me back. Blinking myself back into my body, I slowly opened my eyes but quickly shut them to protect them from the light.

"Kristen, can you open your eyes now?" Dr. R coached.

Keeping one eye shut and opening the other I focused in on the green blob standing at my feet that formed into Dr. Right. Then slowly, I opened the other eye.

"I'm going to tell Mark that you can have a baby any time now." His words floated up through my body and rested in my ears. I smiled a weary smile. "You can rest for a while and then you can go home. I'll see you for a follow-up in my office," he said, squeezing my feet as he disappeared from my sight.

Charlotte was standing beside me, as I tried to regain my awareness to time and place.

"Do I have a sanitary napkin on?" With each word it felt as though I swallowed glass.

"Yes, Kristen."

The thought of being out of control, naked, and having no awareness as to what had occurred shook me. I willed away the uncertainty, falling into denial again.

My body began to shake uncontrollably, my legs wobbled, and my back arched off the bed. Moving in this spastic manner a chill ran up my spine and spread through my torso and limbs.

"It's the anesthesia, I'll go get you some warm blankets, it will stop soon," Charlotte said as she began to drape me with warm white blankets. It was the worst case of chills that I had ever had. As quickly as it began it stopped.

Lying quietly I was still struggling with the lost time. What time is it? What happened to me? Where did I go? That whole train of thought was abruptly stopped when it dawned on me that if I could pee I could go home to the comfort of my own bed.

That became my goal. Urination!

I began to drink– water, ginger ale, and more water. My throat was sore from the breathing tube, it must have scratched my throat while I was intubated. I was on my third glass of water when Mark was brought in to see me.

"Hi, honey, Dr. Right said you did great," leaning over to kiss me. "He gave me these color pictures of the surgery to show you." Mark began showing me my uterus, ovaries, and finally the cysts.

"It was as though a bowling ball was sitting on your tubes, see here, this is the cyst, Dr. Right popped it and cut it away. This picture shows how it looked before and here is after."

The color pictures clearly showed the story. Dr. R. popped the "bowling ball," drained the fluid, and then removed it.

It was amazing to see the whole thing after it was completed. The second entry into our keepsake book. This time it was great news.

"Mark, isn't this unbelievable? This is the first time I've seen my insides. Can you believe that mass of junk was in me?"

Then, "I have to pee," I shouted, totally losing sight of the amazing picture.

"Let's do this slowly, like baby steps," Charlotte's motherly voice warned.

Sitting up, I draped my legs over the side, but finally, "We have to hurry!" I had great urgency.

The sanitary napkin went from the front of me up to my back. I thought it probably could have supported my entire body weight because it was so huge. I had never experienced a product like that. As I walked it stayed in place; I wasn't sure if it was moving and I wasn't or if I was moving and it wasn't.

Entering the bathroom I was in a panic.

"I don't think I can make it, Mark!"

I willed away the pain and accomplished my mission.

I just needed to get dressed and then it would be homeward bound. Whipping open the wooden door, I yelled to Charlotte, "I'm going to Disney!" I giggled while everyone else in the recovery area looked perplexed.

I didn't care what anyone thought, I truly believed Mark and I were now cleared to proceed to our home to create "magic" and our family.

Thank you, God.

Girlfriend to Girlfriend:

Facing surgery ranks right up there with the most stressful experiences in your life.

The denial strategy worked for me, but it was a stupid one! I have a Wonder Woman complex and the idea of being "needy" scares me.

The most important thing to remember is to nurture yourself before, during, and after any procedure or surgery.

My Dr. R. told me I could drive when I felt ready.

Upon hearing that, my daily task was to practice braking the car. I would back out of the garage and pound on the brakes. If I could stand the pain, I reasoned, I could drive. For days following the surgery I tried, and would limp out of the car, back into the house, onto the couch. How stupid!

There was no rush. I suggest you take your time to start your normal daily activities of life, unlike me. It ended up taking me twice as long to recuperate because I wasn't mindful of my body.

One last thing: try to schedule your surgery on a Friday. That way you include two weekend days in your recovery before you have to return to work.

Chapter Five
My First Date with ART

Choose your rut carefully; you'll be in it for the next ten miles.
Road sign, upstate New York

"You have great eggs and you, Mark, have great sperm, it's now a matter of getting them together. Kristen, your hormone levels are perfect and the only real functional issue is your tube. The corrective surgery removed all the cysts and endometrial matter, but I cannot say for certain the right tube is functioning. You could continue to try naturally or we can help with IUI, intrauterine insemination. This would increase the likelihood of conception by placing the grade A sperm through Kristen's cervix into her uterus closer to the egg." The sound of Dr. Right's voice was hypnotic.

"IUI..." I swooned.

"It's an easy procedure, it's done upstairs in the IVF suite. Mark will arrive an hour before the procedure and produce a sample. That sample will have to run an obstacle course and when it's completed the course, the sperm that are left will be the ones with the best mobility and morphology."

Mark and I nodded our heads as if we heard this medical stuff every day. Oh, the old obstacle course, spinning down the sperm, we're very familiar with that.

"Then the sperm will be loaded into a catheter and brought to you and your nurse for insemination. The process begins with a cleaning solution used to wash you out, to avoid having any bacteria introduced into your cervix, and then the catheter will be inserted through your vagina into your cervix and the sperm will be inseminated."

Still shaking our heads, Mark and I agreed that if it would increase our odds of pregnancy then we would do it! This was definitely the next step for us. How hard could an IUI be, anyway?

"I'll be giving you a drug called Clomid to help stimulate your follicles so that your odds of creating a fertilized egg will increase. You'll take pills every day; the nurse will call you daily with your instructions. All this will be explained at the orientation, which is required before you can begin a cycle."

My thoughts began to drift and I imagined Mark and I standing at the ocean's edge on a breathtaking New England day, the sun shining so brightly that it distorted my vision as to where the land ended and the water began. Just our big toes were being rhythmically covered by each wave. "It's kinda cold," I said, giving Mark my weather report.

"You know it's better if you just dive in, you won't notice the temperature," Mark encouraged.

"No, I need to go slowly, don't splash." Mark was taking his direct approach and I was taking my inch-by-inch approach until we were both fully enveloped by the shimmering summer ocean.

That's how our envelopment into ART's world began, with each of us using our own strategies. If I knew then what I know now I would have asked for a life vest.

My fertility was already consuming more of my attention than any other aspect of my life. Mark and I had just started a new company which provided corporate motivational seminars and, to be honest, my focus on this new enterprise was low. Working in our home office, clock-watching the day away, I thought, five more hours and I'll need to leave for the orientation.

Two hours and then I can leave. The big hand on the clock seemed to mock me and move backwards.

"Enough work for today, I must bathe." Rolling out of bed into your home office, there's no commute and no dress code. I worked today in my sweats and Mark's sweat socks. Time to shower. I was filled with anticipation.

Leaning on my forearms, I allowed the water to pour over my shoulders, down my back. The sound of the shower drowned out my inner voice and allowed me to focus on meditating. I revitalized my body, mind, and soul in one long, hot shower.

Choosing my dress with great care, giggling to myself, I got dressed as though going on a date. I would be attending the orientation alone because Mark was away on business. It was my task to obtain the information and then share it with my spouse.

I stood in front of our full-length mirror checking to make sure I looked OK to leave the house. The ring of the phone interrupted my primping.

"Hi, honey," Mark said in a cheerful voice on the other line.

"Hey, baby, where are you?" I asked. It's strange that I often don't know exactly where Mark is. Our new company required him to travel quite extensively and it was hard to keep his schedule straight– and apparently mine as well.

"Don't you remember? I'm in New York."

"Oh, yes, I knew it was some 'New' state. I'm all ready to go."

"Doesn't it start at 6:00 P.M.?" Mark asked.

"No, 7:00 P.M." I replied snippily.

"You better check, honey, I believe it was 6:00 P.M." Mark lobbed back the tennis ball.

"You can't keep track of your schedule, why are you so sure of mine?" I replied. Pulling out the letter from the clinic, my mouth dropped open. It *was* 6:00 P.M. "Oh, my God!" I yelled. "It's 6:00 P.M. and I'm an hour away!"

I glanced down at my watch and began to panic – it was already 5:30 P.M.

"If you leave now you'll be OK," Mark said.

I tore down the cellar stairs, leaving the cellar door open to the garage, my coat dragging along the ground with each step; I vaulted into the car and sped out the driveway!

"Look out!" I yelled at everyone in my way while slipping into my internal dialogue. Miss primping-in-front-of-the-mirror and now you screwed up the first IUI and this opportunity to be a mom. How could you do this Kristen, you watch the clock all day and screwed up! My God, what would you do if you were a mom, leave your child on the roof of the car? Everything was such life and death when it came to my conceiving, all or nothing, black or white.

47

I jumped as my cell phone interrupted me. "Yes?" I knew it was Mark.

"Kristen, I hope you're not driving crazy, we can go to the orientation next month and start then." His voice was calm and authoritative.

"First of all I'm not driving crazy," I said, glancing at the speedometer. I noticed that I was going 85 mph and instantly released the pressure on the gas pedal. "And secondly, what are you, NUTS?! I'm not waiting a month!"

Time was such a priceless commodity; I wanted to be pregnant now, and could not bear to wait 30 days. Thirty days might as well be a lifetime.

"OK, promise me you'll drive safely."

"Yes, I'll drive safely." I was about 15 minutes away and as the words left my mouth I moved into the passing lane and put the pedal to the metal. If I go 85 mph for the next few exits I'll make it in time, I thought to myself.

"You're endangering my life talking to me while I'm driving. I have to go, I'll call you later," I said, throwing the cell phone on the passenger's seat as I gripped the steering wheel tighter and held on for my life.

I arrived at the clinic in 45 minutes. It was 6:15 PM and I ran to the clinic's windowless door and threw it open. The lobby was filled to capacity and instantly the room's attention was drawn in my direction. Almost in unison the group turned around to see who was arriving late. "I'm sorry," I said to the entire room and again to Jennifer as she handed me my orientation packet.

I took a seat on the aisle and glanced at the woman to my right. She was alone too and I made eye contact with her and smiled. My body began to tingle. This was the strangest sensation. I felt as though I was looking into my own eyes and it startled me. Her distant look and sadness were ready to spill out. This complete stranger's eyes, the window to her soul, her longing that she tried to mask so the world wouldn't see, moved me. She quickly looked away, recognizing that I might have gained some private information about her.

I put my head down and placed the gray folder that Jennifer had just given me on my lap and began to flip through the pages.

"We're looking at the yellow page." She addressed the remark to me.

Jennifer, a petite, bubbly nurse, was addressing the group. She looked about 12 years old. I couldn't believe she was old enough to know about human reproduction, let alone get up and speak about it before a group of patients. She was describing timed intercourse and IUI. Her delivery was rapid and well-rehearsed.

"We begin your cycle from the first day of menstruation. This means full flow – enough to soak a sanitary napkin before three o'clock in the afternoon, that's your first day. If you're just spotting, or if it's after three o'clock then it's not considered the first day of your cycle. If the blood is brown and scant, that's not the first day of your cycle either. It should be full flow and the blood should be red. We just use three o'clock as a cut-off point."

I began to scribble notes in the pad in the back of my dayrunner; I was trying to keep up when the information changed to the male partner's responsibilities.

"Men need to arrive an hour before the IUI and produce a sample. You can go directly to the upstairs suite. Remember not to ejaculate immediately before giving the sample. It's good to have ejaculated three days prior but not the previous day."

You could feel the total discomfort as we all squirmed in our seats. The only person who didn't seem uncomfortable was Jennifer. Tossing her long brown hair, she continued.

"If you're starting a course of Clomid, take your first dosage of 50 milligrams on day two of your cycle. You may notice a few side effects, including breast tenderness and mood swings. But what you really want to watch for is the 'halo effect.' That's just what it sounds like – halos around lights, which may be accompanied by blurred vision, nausea, headache, and vomiting. This happens only rarely, but if this does occur with you, call the office right away."

I looked up and the picture of Dr. Right holding twins caught my eye. That will be us next year, I thought to myself and then

49

my mind started to wander. I really don't need this information, I'm just going to go home, take the Clomid, come in for the extra boost of "he man" sperm and then have a torrid night of lovemaking with my husband. BAM! Next month I'll be pregnant.

I was thinking of being in our bed, snuggled close to Mark, my head upon his naked chest, twirling his chest hair in my fingers, when I was abruptly snapped out of my mildly erotic daydream.

Out of the corner of my eye I saw the shine of a needle. What the hell is that? The size of the intermuscular needle made my eyes pop out like a cartoon character. That needs to go where? I had a flashing image of it going straight through my buttocks!

"This needle is used with the drug Profasi, the ovarian stimulation hormone. In layman's terms, this drug makes you ovulate more than one follicle at a time, which in turn increases your likelihood of fertilization and pregnancy."

"Jennifer? Excuse me, Jennifer?" I needed immediate clarification. "I was under the impression that I was only required to take the Clomid because my hormone levels are normal."

"Along with the Clomid, we also have you inject the Profasi," Jennifer replied.

I asked another question, this time slowing my speech. "No, I don't think you understand. Dr. Right said…"

"Kristen, you'll have to call and check with him, but I'm pretty sure everyone will required to inject the hormone."

I suddenly felt sick and began to take more notes and stay focused on the remainder of the information. Next came Jennifer's laundry list of do's and don'ts.

- Don't drink caffeine
- Don't smoke
- Don't drink alcohol
- Don't exercise after the insemination
- Don't go in a hot tub, especially males
- Don't take any over-the-counter pain relievers

- Don't forget your prenatal vitamins
- Don't ejaculate for two days prior to your insemination

I felt totally overwhelmed and wished Mark was with me; I needed his two ears to be hearing this information too. My head was spinning. I just wanted a child. This is way too much!

When the Do's prior to insemination started for the men, there was noticeable change in the back of their heads as they all began to shrink down in their chairs.

Partners' Do's

- Arrive an hour before your scheduled time.
- Go right up to room 205.
- Produce your sample: a.k.a. visit the spank tank. Your sperm needs to be less than five days old and at least as old as three days old—in other words, you can ejaculate five days prior but not one or two days before.

The image of the entire room looking at a calendar and trying to arrange the best catch of sperm for their insemination made me cringe. It was so cold and strange. We were strangers knowing way too much information about each other.

Jennifer then shifted gears and began to inform us about the consent forms.

"These need to be signed and witnessed by the nurse prior to beginning the cycle. If you'd like to take them with you, you may, but you cannot begin the cycle without the signed, witnessed consent form in your file. We're going to begin injection techniques now for those needing nightly injections. If this does not pertain to you, you may leave. One last thing, I'll be your primary nurse in the monitoring room, so if you have any questions or concerns please feel free to call. Thank you!" Thinking she had been wrong about me needing to take the Profasi, I decided to not stay for the injection details.

It was over and I felt heavy in my chair. There certainly wasn't any warm fuzzy part of ART's orientation. I realized that we were definitely entering a clinical, mechanical process.

I wondered if I would ever be passionate about making love again. It seemed to me that it was now pure mechanics: Mark will visit the spank tank again, his product will be refined, I will take the Clomid and super ovulate, and they will be put together through science.

I was shaking as I put my coat on and walked, dazed, to the car. I drove a slow 60 mph home in the middle lane of the highway. The ride was a blur.

I collected my folder and prescriptions and entered our house, reached for the phone without removing my coat, and called Mark.

"I've been waiting for you, how was it?" There was excitement in his voice, in direct contrast to mine.

"I feel totally overwhelmed, Mark. I wish you were there," I mumbled.

"I'm sorry, honey, can you tell me about it?" he said.

"NO, not now, tomorrow. I need to go to sleep."

"What do we need to do first?" Mark asked.

"Just wait for my period to start, I guess," I replied.

Girlfriend to Girlfriend:

Mark and I came to an understanding that we would experience three IUIs and then move on to IVF. But we did so in the heat of an emotional crisis. Hence, our fertility game plan was born. A fertility game plan is a predetermined course of action that both parties agree upon. I would encourage you to take your time and read about all the necessary procedures that might be recommended for your circumstances. Schedule a meeting with your doctor to discuss what he or she is thinking for you down the road if your current course of action does not result in a positive pregnancy test.

Committing everything to writing is a must, as is keeping the fertility game plan handy for constant review. It is also important to bring this with you on your consultations with your Doctor Right. He or she will know the path that is appropriate for you and might have helpful suggestions to add.

We decided that three IUIs and three IVFs would do it for us. Simultaneously, we began educating ourselves about adoption. I'll remember Mark's words forever, the words I needed to hear: "Kristen, I promise next year at this time you'll be a mom, I'll be a dad and our family will begin to grow."

It added to my sense of control when I felt totally out of control. I knew come hell or high water I would be a mom.

How to Get Started
Schedule time with your partner or spouse.
Discuss the following and commit to paper.

How long are you willing to devote to this process as a couple? What are your limits? Individually? Emotionally? Spiritually? What could be your personal signal that you are feeling overwhelmed? How should the dissemination of information be handled? Would you speak with the doctor directly if you were the person who had a procedure? If you feel it is all right to have your partner receive information, how do you want it relayed to you? (Try to elevate the situation that both Mark and I were placed in when I received the call from Dr. Wrong about Mark's test results.) We live in a state where fertility treatments are covered by our insurance. I feel for you if there is an added financial burden. How much are you financially able to invest in this process? What can your budget handle?

Fertility Game Plan
Would you consider a surrogate mom?
Would you use donor sperm?
Would you use donor eggs?
How do you feel about multiple births?
How many eggs would you implant?
Would you selectively reduce?
What are your thoughts about assisted hatching?
Discuss what you would expect from each other in these critical situations– an ectopic pregnancy or a miscarriage.
What would be your stopping point?
What strategies for compromise would you implement if this stopping point is not agreed upon?

53

Questions for Your Doctor

What were your experiences with other patients with similar issues?

What tests or procedures would you recommend for us?

What medications typically are associated with those procedures?

What is the time frame for these procedures?

Chapter Six
ART's Drug Gone Bad!

*Grant me the courage not to give up even though I think it is
hopeless.*
Chester W. Nimitz (1885-1966)

It all began with me reaching under our vanity for the box of
tampons. My obsessing was over–we would definitely be
beginning our first IUI cycle today. The blood was bright red
and it was before three o'clock in the afternoon. Reaching for
the phone, I had the strangest feeling, a mix of power and
disappointment. I had believed we would conceive this month,
but the thoughts that formed at the orientation had propelled me
to anticipate the IUI. I had viewed it as a sure thing. Us,
infertile, NO, we're just slow starters, fertility is my middle
name, hell, I have to always be thinking did I bring my birth
control? Denial would be the strategy of choice to make it
through the insemination.

"Monitoring Room, this is Jennifer, how may I help you?"

"Hi, Jennifer, this is Kristen Magnacca calling, this is day
one of my period, we're scheduled to begin our first cycle with
Clomid."

"OK, Kristen, you're experiencing full flow?"

"Sure am," I replied.

"OK, do you have all your prescriptions?"

"Yes, I need to fill the Clomid, though."

"OK, go ahead and do that and we'll see you tomorrow for
blood work and a vaginal ultrasound."

"Thank you!" Placing the phone down on the kitchen island,
I immediately reached for my informational folder, prescriptions,
and preparations.

1. Clomid prescription, check.
2. Profosi prescription, check (even though I still didn't
   think I'd need it).
3. Intermuscular needle prescription, ouch and check.

4. Alcohol to clean the surface, check.
5. Alcohol to clean the outside of the medicine container, check.
6. An old laundry detergent container for the used needles, check. In all my existence the knowledge of how to dispose of used hypodermic needles did not seem necessary until now.

"Put them in an old laundry detergent container and call your city or town to determine how to dispose of hazardous waste," Jennifer explained at the orientation. I will be producing hazardous waste, who knew!

As I stood before these keys that would unlock our destiny to our child I thought, Tomorrow is our day to begin our cycle and produce our child. The denial strategy was coloring my understanding of the actual process of intrauterine insemination; I thought all I needed to do was to swallow the Clomid capsule which would equal an instant pregnancy.

Bounding out of bed and into the shower, I felt my old self appear with the excitement of the new beginning. I will manage this month's intrauterine insemination and then complete the month pregnant. That was my mantra.

Absolutely nothing in life will prepare you for the indignity of experiencing a vaginal ultrasound while menstruating.

I arrived at the clinic through the traffic mayhem. The morning commute east into the Boston area was crazed.

Grace escorted me into her galley laboratory, the grey cabinets covered with cartoons as well as the wall immediately to the left. The cartoons were to distract the current occupant of the blood chair for a moment while the needle was being inserted.

Grace immediately went to work labeling the glass vials while I pushed up my sleeves. Tying the rubber strap around my upper arm, she said, "Nice veins" with a smile.

"Thanks," I smiled back. It was quick and painless, so to speak.

Placing the vial into the holding rack, Grace directed, "You can wait here for Denise, she'll do your ultrasound next." I settled into the corner chair and reached into the basket on the floor for a magazine.

"Next," Denise called. "Do you need to use the ladies' room?"

I used the restroom and met Denise in the examination room.

"You can remove your clothes from the waist down and drape this over your lap," she said, handing me a sheet.

It all of a sudden occurred to me that I was menstruating. Full flow, fully flowing, you could call me Flow!

"Denise, I'm having my period..." I said questioningly. Like she didn't know that!

"That's OK, Kristen, just sit on this pad."

I followed the procedure, arranging myself on the quilted pad, and closed my eyes. I felt so uneasy about this situation. I could just image standing up to a bloody mess.

Denise returned and nonchalantly slipped a condom on the probe, smeared it with KY jelly, then inserted it into my vagina on its reconnaissance mission.

Instantly I took a "mind vacation." It's a technique I use to get through embarrassing situations. I was immediately on the beach of Saint Croix, enjoying the sun on my face and the breeze through my hair.

"OK, Kristen, all set, you can get dressed now," Denise's voice whispered.

Alone in the examination room, I stood up with the protective pad wedged between my thighs and immediately started to clean up the K-Y jelly and menstrual remnants.

That night my instructions were left on the answering machine. "Kristen, this is the nurse from your doctor's office. He would like you to take two capsules tonight and we'll see you the next day for blood, call if you have any questions." Beep.

I followed the instructions and took one Clomid and then another. As the water swirled around in my mouth I imaged this little pill traveling through my body and cheering all the way. "Go, go, go get them, we'll shake you up! We'll shake you up!"

And my ovaries cheering, "Help is on the way!" There was inner excitement!

Working in our un-air-conditioned home office the next day in June, I felt incredibly hot. I was perspiring more than normal and as I glanced up at the computer screen, I felt as though my eyes were moving in slow motion. I did work late last night and woke up early, I rationalized. Plus, it's so warm today. Reaching for our green bank deposit envelope, I decided that it was time to run errands, in the air-conditioned car and bank.

The line at the bank was longer than usual. If it weren't for the quarterly taxes being due I would have turned and used the ATM machine instead. As I waited in line with my envelope, I began to notice a halo effect around the lights. I instantly removed my glasses and cleaned them, a task that doesn't get done on a regular basis. That didn't seem to help. It must be the heat, I thought.

Blaming the heat again, I transformed my envelope into a fan. The breezes from my makeshift fan relieved some discomfort, but my vision was still distorted.

As the banking line slowly snaked its way through the velvet ropes I began my mental Ping-Pong. Leave, stay, let's leave, you better stay, you'll have to come back tomorrow, leave. I'm not feeling so good.

My voice turned stern. You haven't eaten anything for breakfast and it's now approaching 1:00 P.M. You're just hungry! That's what it is.

"Next," the bank teller called. It was my turn. The banking transactions finally completed, I placed the slips into the envelope and turned to leave. The halos were bigger and I could see a lightening bolt on my peripheral vision. Sweat formed on the back of my neck, and I wiped it away with my hand. The heat usually doesn't bother me this much, I thought.

I rushed through the grocery store, conveniently located next door to the bank. Grabbing a bagel and bottled water, I began eating prior to my turn in the express check-out lane.

My vision was blurred and my head began to pound. A wave of panic washed over me. "I don't think I can drive home,"

I said out loud. I sat in the car and wolfed the remaining half of the bagel and drained the water. Reaching for my seatbelt, I totally lost all vision in my right eye and began to cry.

It dawned on me that I was feeling a migraine coming on like a speeding train down the track. I drove home with one eye closed and parked the car in the garage. Navigating the stairs into our house with the one eye still closed, I relied on my other senses to help. I felt as though I was swaying back and forth with each step while the room was spinning in the opposite direction. I crashed onto our family room's couch, reaching for the phone. I squinted while I dialed the clinic's number.

"May I please speak to Jennifer?" I asked.

"She's not available, may I help?" the nurse's voice replied.

"This is Kristen Magnacca and I just started my first IUI cycle. I seem to be experiencing a migraine and halo vision. I have a feeling that the Clomid and I are not getting along."

"How many pills have you taken?" she asked.

"Two," I answered.

"Well, it can't be the Clomid, it must be the heat. You've only taken a mild dose. Why don't you rest for a while and call us back and let us know how you're feeling?"

"OK," I mumbled.

Girlfriend to Girlfriend:

Be your own advocate! I can't stress this enough. When you know, you know. It was not the heat– I've lived through 34 summers in Massachusetts and never once experienced a migraine from heat! The only difference was the Clomid. You know your body the best, and you know when something isn't right. Push the envelope.

It is an extremely rare occurrence that someone has such a strong reaction to Clomid. I would have to be in the two percent of women who would experience the serious side effect.

The one thing that Mark and I will strongly recommend is that you keep in mind that your doctor and nurses are there for you, but there are also a lot of other patients that they have to attend to. Listen to your heart and trust your instincts for all medications and medical procedures. Try to listen to your inner voice, the intuitive one, and don't get railroaded into a procedure or situation that you're not comfortable with. Trust the little hairs on the back of your neck and your "gut" reaction.

I lay on my back on our couch for what seemed like a lifetime, totally unsure of what to do. As I rolled to my side, the room followed in slow motion; my stomach jumped. My vision was gone and the aura was present in full force. Starting to dial Mark's pager number by feel, I laid the phone down and pushed myself up.

I was trying to remain in control but started to sob. I put my arms out in front of me and began to feel my way up the stairs. Our bedroom was only a few steps away but it felt like miles.

I was sure someone had hit my stomach with a bat. I started to vomit and there was no way to maintain my composure until a receptacle could be used. I tossed my water and bagel all over the stairway. I managed to make it into our bathroom and was sick into the toilet; wiping my mouth, I crawled to bed.

The pounding in my head was so loud; I pushed on both sides of my head with my hands, and began to cry uncontrollably.

Then I got sick again, this time off the side of our bed, missing our trash basket. I frantically called Mark on his cell phone.

"Help!" I cried when he answered the phone. "Mark, something is terribly wrong. I can't stop–" My sentence was interrupted as I got sick again.

"Hang on, baby, I'll be home in 25 minutes!" Mark shouted.

Hearing Mark screech into the driveway and race up the stairs 20 minutes later, I began to cry even harder. Physically weak and emotionally drained from vomiting for one and half hours, I was a basket case. I thought for sure that we would start seeing internal organs in our trash basket.

I continued being sick until dawn of the next morning, June 10th, which so happened to be our wedding anniversary.

"This is Mark Magnacca calling. My wife, Kristen, called yesterday with halo vision and vomiting. We just started our first cycle of IUI with Clomid; she won't be taking that drug any more. And I'll need to speak with Dr. Right as soon as possible." The authoritative tone echoed throughout our bedroom.

"OK, Mr. Magnacca, I'll have Dr. Right call you back."

"Kristen, what is going on with you?" It was the concerned voice of Dr. Right.

To tell the truth, my heart skipped a beat. I was infatuated with my endocrinologist. "I'm not getting along too well with the Clomid, it started with halo vision, a migraine, and then moved south to my stomach."

"OK, I want you to stop taking the Clomid, you're experiencing a rare side effect from it."

"I'm never taking that again!" I exclaimed.

"Fine," he reassured.

"Do we stop this cycle? I don't want to stop."

"You can continue with this cycle drug-free and be inseminated after blood monitoring and a shot of Profosi."

"A shot of the Profosi? I thought I wasn't required to take that shot?"

"Kristen, we must have had a miscommunication, you will need to take the injection."

"Are you sure?"

"Yes, you'll need to take the Profosi and the next day you'll be inseminated."

"That sounds like a plan, thank you!" My hand rested on the white phone receiver a little too long. It was going to be too much effort to move it from this position.

"Hey, baby, are you going to start to get ready?"

Rolling in the direction of Mark's voice, "Did you get the number of the truck?" I mumbled.

"What?" he replied, totally confused.

"Did you get the number of the truck?" I mumbled again.

"What are you talking about?"

"Did you get the number of the truck that hit me?"

"Do you still want to go to Cape Cod for our anniversary, Kristen?" Mark questioned.

"Most certainly– do you still want to take me after seeing me look like Sybil barfing up pea soup?"

I felt as though I had one hell of a night of drinking and dancing but could not remember the fun.

As we reached the other side of the bridge, the childhood song of "The Bear Went over the Mountain" started to play in my head. The only thing the bear could see was the other side of the mountain, but what I could see was relaxation and freedom. The Sagamore Bridge, the entrance into Cape Cod, had the same effect as Valium on every inch of my body.

As the sea air drifted through the open car window it brought with it a natural incense which made the inside of my nose come to life. The smell of salt air, the sun shimmering on the ocean, and the boats leaving their white wake behind them distracted my state and washed away the previous day's disaster. We were headed back to our place, the safety and solitude of Cape Cod. It was our anniversary and the ocean area held such wonderful, treasured memories. We had decided to give each other an experience that neither one of us had experienced before and visit a referred "friend of a friend" who had the gift of clairvoyance.

I had made the appointment with Dede and informed Mark of the time and place. We were both willing participants but I was still feeling nervous about the meeting. It provided a much-needed distraction from our fertility challenges and I was hoping she would "see" into our situation, but not see too much.

We traveled down Route 6, the highway through Cape Cod, driving past my family's exit, down towards Provincetown. With our hands lying together on Mark's thigh, I began to get lost in the replay of our wedding.

The movie played in fast forward in little snippets. My little nephew, George, pushing his energy at Mark. "It's not fair, I was in the limo first, I get to ride with Cocci to the reception."

"Not this time, pal, we'll see you there!"

George's face pressing up against the window with a serious pout. Mark then pushing the button to close the window

62

between the driver and us so that we could kiss in private. Then the total feeling of joy.

My eyes began to water.

"What?" Mark said leaning over to confirm my tears.

"I was just watching our wedding video," I replied.

Mark understands that I am a very visual person and experience life repeatedly through what I have seen and then what I have felt.

"What part were you watching?" he asked.

"Remember our ride to the reception?" I questioned.

"Yes…" It was a naughty *yes*.

"That part," I smiled.

"Oh! I love you, Kristen. It will be OK." Mark squeezed my hand.

We arrived at Dede's house and it was not what I expected. I really wasn't sure what I was expecting, but it was not that. The gravel driveway crunched when we pulled in and parked next to her red Volvo station wagon. I guess I didn't expect a clairvoyant to be driving a Volvo. What did I expect?

Her garden showed its love and care. My glance stayed on the garden decoration of a dragon as we walked up Dede's brick steps. The dragon's head and humps were visible and my imagination picked up and formed its feet and undercarriage beneath the ground.

Fletcher's large bark greeted us first and then Dede swung open the door. Fletcher stood shoulder level with me and his dark eyes looked straight into mine.

"Hi, I'm Dede and this is Fletcher, he's just getting to know you."

Her smiling, soulful, blue eyes danced with each word. I instantly felt naked in front of her, as if she could see straight through me into my heart. There was no apprehension, just a brief flutter of energy. It was warm and healing.

As we followed Dede up into her reading room I noticed her décor. The furnishings were unique and I wanted to ask about each piece. They looked as though they held some secret, some history or knowledge.

The smell of sage greeted me with my first step into the room. I glanced at Mark and could read his mind—he thought that the smell was marijuana.

We arranged ourselves next to each other on the white two-person couch. The throw pillows and blankets looked inviting. I admired the painting above Dede's pastel chair and looked up at her books organized on her shelves. "Got it, read that one, got it." I started to take mental inventory of her books.

I felt comfortable and strange at the same time. I wanted to hear, to hear about everything but I also wanted not to hear about everything.

My interest in the psychic world had been present for some time and had actually been piqued when my mother purchased her house on the Cape years before.

The ranch house was in a great location, just a few minutes' walk to the beach, but it had been left unloved for some time. The couple who had built the house and lived in it all their lives had passed over, first the wife and then the husband. My mother and stepfather purchased the house knowing that work needed to be done.

On weekends we would drive down to the Cape and work all weekend beautifying the tired-looking home. Prior to meeting Mark, I would drive down Friday nights after working all week and begin my weekend project. Some nights I would be the first to open the house from the previous weekend and would have the strange feeling of walking into a home with someone else already there. Chalking it up to being tired, I overlooked those feelings until the day I was exiting the back bedroom, which we called "the commune" because it could hold a queen bed, a full bed, a twin bed, and a crib. It was large enough to accommodate half of our family.

Out of the corner of my eye I saw him. He was standing in the corner wearing a flannel shirt. I squinted and blinked and he was gone. "I must be exhausted," I thought and walked into the bathroom.

A short time after my first sighting I saw him again. This time I not only saw him, I felt him. I felt him just as you would feel the breeze from someone, anyone, walking past you.

"Ma, did the man who used to live here die in this house?" We were in the kitchen, my mother's back to me; she was making us each a cup of morning tea.

"Who told you?" she snapped, as if I had done something wrong.

"Well, he's here," I replied. I knew from her reaction that she knew it too.

It was the strangest thing. I was not afraid of him, I felt as though he needed our help, that he had some unfinished business, so I began including him in our decisions regarding household renovations.

"Hey, Milton, we're going to redo the bathroom floor. I think the pink squares would accent the tile, how about you?"

And so began my speaking to spirits and also my questioning about what happens to you after you die. My religious upbringing teaches that you hang around, either in Purgatory or Hell, waiting for the Judgment Day and your old body back. Somehow that didn't seem all that likely to me.

My sister and I began to read about another recovering Catholic, George Anderson, who also has the gift of clairvoyance.

I befriended Milton and felt sorry for his confusion and loneliness. Other members in my family didn't take to him so easily. Maybe Dede could give voice to him and help me help him, I thought.

"I'll need something from each of you."

I rolled my wedding ring off my finger and handed to Dede. Mark's left elbow provided me with a sharp jab in my side as he removed his.

I was skeptical and excited at the same time. She began with some of Mark's issues and then moved on to ours.

"Kristen, why don't you believe that you can have a child? What are you doing to yourself?" Then I felt the presence of my wonderful grandfather and nearly dropped off the couch.

"Red Topper, you're going to have a baby, a son. Stop doing this to yourself, you are so worthy."

I began to sob; it was as though my soul had opened, revealing the dark area of hurt to the light, forcing me to face it.

65

I knew as soon as she called me "Red Topper" that it was my grandfather. I hadn't heard or thought of that nickname in a decade. I was his Red Topper and he was my hero, my saving grace. I had to believe him, but the dark, dangerous part of my soul was still present, along with my fear.

"You have to stop taking whatever medication that you were taking. Your constitution is very sensitive to that, it's not helpful."

I nearly died. How did she know about what had just happened the day before?

Looking up, I smoothed out the wrinkles in my jean dress. Was it hearing my grandfather or was it the culmination of all the heartbreak the day before? Was she reading my mind or my future?

"Your son is with you now, Kristen," she confirmed. "He's a friend to you and Mark, he'll bring joy to your life and provide laughter where there really isn't much now. He'll slow your pace and make you stop and smell the roses, so to speak. Would you call him Cole?"

"I will call him whatever he wishes if he just would come."

"Well, he is coming," she confirmed again.

"Thank God," I cried.

We were still shaking when we got back to our car. It had been an amazing experience and an emotional one, too. Mark and I had both believed we had heard from the other side, a sign that life does go on and that we are able to communicate when our physical body is not on this plane.

We drove in silence down a road that we had been numerous times. But it was the first time we noticed the street sign "Cole's Way." It was as if the spiritual world was sending us a sign: It will be all right.

I regained my confidence and looked forward to continuing our first IUI without the Clomid.

"It's going to work, I can feel it!"

Girlfriend to Girlfriend:

66

Trying to temper your optimism and remain hopeful at the same time is a fine line that even a professional tightrope walker would not be able to walk.

Keep referring back to your fertility game plan to remain in control and focused on your outcome.

To constantly reframe our situation, Mark and I used visualization to help us through the rough spots. My husband is in the motivational seminar business, which is kind of ironic, considering what we were going through; within his seminar he discusses how peak performers, especially Olympic athletes, use visualization before and during an event. The idea is to replay the scene in you head with the outcome that you desire. I would replay standing in our bathroom, leaning on our vanity, waiting the appropriate minutes to see the two purple lines appear on the white pregnancy wand. It helped to do this when I was too focused on the negative aspects of our fertility challenges. I found it provided me with a mental break and refocused my train of thought.

I would also visualize my blood being drawn without pain, the vaginal ultrasounds being completed without embarrassment or discomfort, and prior to an insemination I would visualize my egg being surrounded by Mark's "he-man" sperm.

Think about each event and play it out in your mind's eye prior to actually experiencing it. It will give you confidence and a sense of security.

Chapter Seven
Friends of ART's

When people have light in themselves, it will shine out from them. Then we get to know each other as we walk together in the darkness....
    Albert Schweitzer (1875-1965)

"Please refrain from sharing." The black-lettered sign in the clinic reminded me of the "Don't feed the animals" sign at the zoo.

It was the understanding at our clinic not to engage in conversation with fellow patients. Biting my lower lip as I read the sign, I thought, God, I broke that rule a million times. I guess it's to discourage hurt feelings and protect patient confidentiality if you aren't the patient blessed enough to obtain pregnancy. It's a stupid rule, though – where else could I feel as though I wasn't the only women not to make it into the sorority? I mean, each and every day for blood work and ultrasounds I'm surrounded by women who feel what I'm feeling and have experienced the same procedures – these women are my partners in fertility.

"What are you in for?" I whispered to the woman seated next to me. I felt as though I was back in my Catholic school uniform, sneaking a note to my friend during class, trying not to be found out by Sister Etheltrude.

The woman mumbled, "IUI" and put her head down. She acted as if she were on a plane and was faking reading her book to avoid conversation.

As I glanced around the room, the nervous energy was palpable. I saw her yesterday, her too, I thought. It was driving me crazy to see the same women day in and day out and not know their circumstances. What's their situation? How long has she been trying? What is she in for?

Glancing down at my *People* magazine, I saw Bill Murray staring back. Then laughter filled my thoughts as my inner voice disguised itself to that of a deep male voice: "The part of Bill

Murray in *Groundhog Day* will be played by Kristen Magnacca."

The plot of that movie mimicked my daily life. I imagined myself being Bill Murray's character each morning, experiencing the same rituals. Our alarm rings and then I roll away from spooning Mark, bounding out of the warmth of our bed into the shower, then racing down the stairs, putting on the tea water, filling my travel mug while grabbing a granola bar. Then I scurry down the cellar stairs into my car, race out of the driveway, down our street, and begin to wait in traffic on my daily way to the clinic for more tests. It was a "hurry up and wait" game every morning, repeating itself morning after morning. I was living the same stuck feeling that Bill Murray's character had experienced.

In order to break the monotony I created a "beat the fellow infertility women" game to add some excitement to the mundane experience. My imaginary game went as follows: If I arrived first or second each morning, I would win and life would be good.

For some strange reason my place in line became so important to me. I felt as though it was the one and only thing that I could control in the revolving world. Mark and I were told when to have sex, what to eat, and when not to exercise. But my space in line was mine, all mine. I staked my claim on my spot, my territory, my domain. I wondered if this line of thinking bordered on a psychological disorder.

On the fourth day of my cycle I decided to sit in a new seat in the ultrasound waiting area when she appeared again. I had watched her, this tall, very thin, attractive woman, for days.

Our chairs arranged like in a train compartment, I was diagonally across from her.

When the woman directly across from me sneezed, "God bless you," the tall woman and I said at the same time.

There was no response from the sneezing woman but the tall, thin woman and I locked eyes.

"What are you in for?" I asked with a broad smile.

"IUI," she answered, looking as though she was a deer staring into the headlights of an oncoming car.

"How many have you had?" I pounced.

"This will be our third," she whispered.

"This is our first. Who's your doctor? What medications are you taking? What time do you inject?"

She answered each one of my questions.

I was filled with excitement when Denise called my name for my ultrasound.

I was in and out, whim, wham, thank you ma'am, the ultrasound was over and I was done for the morning.

"My name's Kristen." I stopped and took the chair I had waited in.

"I'm Maria," she replied slowly while sizing me up, not sure if I was planning on robbing her or something along those lines.

"Nice to meet you, I guess I'll see you tomorrow," I smiled once again.

"Bye?" she replied with a question.

I was walking on air! I had found a new fertility friend!

The sound of Mark fumbling for the alarm clock woke me. I was momentarily disoriented as to what day it was.

"Is today Friday?" I yawned at Mark.

"It's Saturday," he yawned back.

"Oh my God, get up!" I cried, running for the bathroom.

On the weekends, all the satellite offices were closed, which required an hour-long drive to the main fertility clinic.

"We don't have time for a shower, let's get going or we'll miss the courier!" I was frantic.

"Calm down," Mark, Mr. Kinethestic, replied.

"Don't tell me to calm down!" I screamed while pulling on my sweatshirt and sweatpants.

"Where's my baseball hat? Where's my baseball hat?" I was screaming while running down the stairs into the kitchen.

"Let's GO!"

The garage door opened in slow motion and we were on our way within ten minutes.

We screeched into the parking lot on two wheels. Mark and I ran into the clinic. There was standing room only while the foyer of the clinic became a makeshift waiting area. Signing in and looking for a waiting spot, I spotted Maria.

"Mark, Mark, that's Maria!" I said with the excitement of a child seeing Santa Claus.

"Relax, Kristen, take a breath, you don't want her to think you're a psycho," he said, smiling.

I then noticed the women in all forms of waiting. There was the ones staring into air or staring at an open magazine and then the ones leaning on their partners. As I was noticing their affects I also noticed their outfits. The women were all put together right. They looked showered and bathed, hair done, makeup and clothes that didn't look like they slept in them.

"We look like hell," I mouthed to Mark.

"We had an hour's drive, Kristen."

"I'm so embarrassed."

Mark rolled his eyes at me and then I spotted another couple dressed in the same apparel. "Thank God."

"Mark, come with me while I talk to Maria."

I crossed the room and found a seat closer to her.

"Hi, Maria, how are you today?"

"Luke, this is Kristen, Kristen, this is my husband, Luke." I could have done the dance of joy!

"Luke, I want you to meet my husband Mark, Mark this is Maria."

"Great to meet you."

Our meeting felt like home but was interrupted by Maria's name being called.

"I would love to continue our conversation," I said.

"Well, here's my number, you could call me at home," Maria answered.

I was overjoyed while we exchanged numbers.

The day of our insemination arrived and it turned out that Maria and I were scheduled on the same day, fifteen minutes apart. The scheduling for the IUIs meant that Maria and I would arrive approximately at the same time for our blood to be drawn and that our husbands would be visiting the clinic's spank tank area also at the same time. There was no pre-planning to this; it was spontaneous, without awkwardness.

Kissing goodbye in the car, Mark and I went to our prospective destinations. Walking with a direct purpose and speed, I arrived in the blood lab, pulled up my sleeve, and immediately began asking what would become my standard pre-insemination question.

"How many women got pregnant last month?"

"I think five or six?" The blood room nurse went straight to work while I looked away as the blood was drawn, painless and easy for me. Not necessarily so for the woman next to me whose arm was being manipulated to produce a large vein. I bent my elbow and held the white gaze with my left pointing finger. Applying pressure, I opened the door and pushed the elevator button. Exiting the elevator I entered the IUI and IVF suite.

Taking a seat with my back to the window I greeted the red-haired nurse/receptionist.

"My husband is back there, isn't he?" I questioned.

"He just went back," she responded with a smile.

It was so strange – Mark was in the spank tank ejaculating without me, and here we were openly discussing it as if he was getting a haircut.

"He's almost done, just needs a blow dry," I thought.

I began to anticipate the outcome of our insemination and daydream about our life with a child when the door swung open.

"Maria," I smiled.

"Kristen, I didn't know you were here," she replied. "Luke's back there," tilting her head to the right.

"So is Mark," I replied.

"Do you think they're in the same room?" We laughed.

Out of the corner of my eye I could see Luke coming to join us. We brushed over the surrealness of the moment.

"Hey, Luke."

"Hi, Kristen." Such a normal exchange of conversation.

Luke and Maria sat down next to me and we all fumbled with the magazines when Mark appeared. It was a repeat of our greeting and then a lull in the conversation.

73

Both men's samples needed to be put through the obstacle course and then loaded into the syringe for insemination. The whole process took about an hour. Cooling our heels in the waiting area was not the best use of this time.

"Do you guys want to go get some coffee, decaf?" Mark asked.

"Sounds like a plan!" We all leapt out of our chairs.

The smell of coffee filled the shop along with the sound of the cappuccino machine.

"Doesn't that sound remind you of the cleansing solution noise before the insemination?" I asked Maria.

"Yes!" she squealed as we both broke into a fit of laughter. Our laughter was filled with both embarrassment and compassion. We glanced around at our fellow coffee drinkers and really didn't care who overheard or who didn't. The fact that we were being "heard" for the first time in a long time created an instant connection. I was so thankful for our developing friendship.

Choosing seats next to the condiment area, Maria and I sat on the same side of the table when our laughter interrupted Mark and Luke's conversation. With smiles, both husbands asked in stereo, "What are you two laughing about?"

We were acting like schoolgirls and making no apologies for our behavior. What a great stress release prior to insemination; releasing all the nervous energy through laughter had to improve our chances of conceiving.

"The sound of the cappuccino machine sounds like the Bentedine solution the nurse uses to clean you out prior to the insemination!" Maria and I laughed again. It wasn't as funny to our husbands. They lost themselves again into their own separate conversation.

"I had a varicocele too, I thought that was what a normal testicle felt like. Dr. L., my urologist, diagnosed it in a matter of seconds and then performed the surgery," Mark responded.

"He was my doctor too," Luke shared.

As our husbands talked, Maria bumped me with her elbow. Glancing at me, she silently indicated to look at the condiment table. The gentleman putting milk or cream and sugar in his coffee was working frantically to get his lid on his cup and out of the shop. As the words *testicle, varicocele,* and *urologist* filled the air, his discomfort level was apparently rising. This threw us into another laughing fit while our husbands sat in total confusion. With a deep breath, both Maria and I tried to bring them up to speed as to what was occurring behind then. We failed to communicate the scene and began to laugh again.

It had been so long since Mark had seen that side of me, I could feel his enjoyment in just watching us experience a moment of happiness. It was the first time in a long time that I had such a good laugh or even something to laugh about. The hour was filled with conversation and before we knew it was time for our inseminations.

"Call me later," I said over my shoulder as Mark and I walked away to the procedure room.

"Good luck," we all said in unison.

Girlfriend to Girlfriend:

One wish for you is that you allow. Allow time not to be your keeper, allow your relationship to be the priority, not your childlessness, and allow others to help.

I encourage you to begin scheduling something fun, silly, and outrageous for you and your partner. It doesn't have to cost a lot of money, it doesn't have to be for a long block of time, but it does have to be something you look forward to each week, something you can count on to build you up personally and as a couple.

Here are my top ten picks to keep your mind off of babymaking:
1) *A long hot bath or shower together or alone*
2) *Blow drying each other's hair*
3) *A foot massage*
4) *A long walk together*
5) *Picnic*
6) *The movies*
7) *An ice cream sundae or some decadent dessert*

8) *Getting dressed up for no apparent reason*

9) *Wear sexy underwear for your enjoyment only*

10) *The most important: I encourage you to begin and stay with your daily journal! In my experience, it washed away all the negative feelings and emotions that accumulated during the day. As I said before, I began each entry with five things that I am thankful for, just common, take-for-granted things. It helped shift my thinking to the positive and helped me focus on my abundance.*

Chapter Eight
ART Will Break Your Heart

If at first you don't succeed try, try, again.
William Edward Hickson (1803-1870)

The heat from the new recessed lighting of the kitchen made painting just that more uncomfortable. Standing in our kitchen which was bare down to the floor and in total disarray, I mumbled to myself, "This is the perfect time to paint" as a form of encouragement. I was creating our dream kitchen, choosing a soft green to accent the granite countertop.

Finished stirring the paint, I delicately poured it into the paint pan and began to apply the fresh color to the corner when Mark bounded into the kitchen.

"Honey, I was just on the phone with my mother, and she's concerned because no one on our side of the family is doing anything for Sharon."

"What?"

I was engrossed in making sure my edging didn't hit the white ceiling and felt as though I was walking into a movie half over.

"I just hung up with my mother, who heard from Scott that Sharon is upset because no one is doing anything for her."

"Mark, are you asking me to give a baby shower?"

I imagined myself with raw nerves exposed like gaping wounds, wounds of childlessness. Placing my hands on my hips and staring at Mark, I heard him reply, "I know, I know, Kristen, but it is my brother and his wife and…"

My inner voice immediately took over. Kristen, what would Jesus do? He would throw her a shower, it's the right thing to do, OK?

"I'll do the shower, is that what you came in for?" I replied with paint dripping onto my sneaker. "I'll do a baby shower for Sharon." I turned back to my wall.

"Are you crazy?" Maria's voice jumped out of the phone at me later.

"I guess I am, can you believe it?" I answered.

Maria, my constant companion on trips to the mall when I could not even look at a pregnant woman.

"Avert your eyes," I would whisper in her ear. "Three o'clock, coming straight at us."

Gripping my arm, she would navigate us in a different direction, straight into the path of a mother and baby.

"Can't they just stay home?" I would beg.

And there we were, the two infertile women, Maria and I, standing in front of the rack containing baby shower paraphernalia. It never dawned on me how stupid this whole situation was. It was bad enough for me to have to prepare for a baby shower, but to drag Maria along – what was wrong with me?

Both of our cycles had resulted in a negative outcome. My blood hormone level remained too high, resulting in a mini-vacation from our fertility challenges. This was also the month's break for Maria and Luke. They would be entering the world of IVF.

So there she and I stood, choosing napkins, invitations, and paper plates to decorate for my husband's brother's wife's baby shower. Never mind purchasing the shower gift as well, bringing me into the baby section of the local department stores.

Then I began my next cycle, our second. Due to the reaction with the Clomid, we progressed to the drug Fertinex, as well as the Profasi injections after all. Looking back, I really wished I had stayed for the injection technique part of the orientation.

My litany of ultrasounds, daily blood work, nightly injections, hormonal eruptions, and eating constraints fell right on schedule.

In the middle of all this, plus working with Mark on our growing motivational seminar business, I was preparing for the event I was dreading, the baby shower. How I wanted it to be me that would be receiving the gifts for our child. The items that I purchased smelled already of baby. My days were an emotional roller coaster, the logical Kristen vs. the emotional

78

Kristen. I was angry and full of envy and longing to be the one that the shower was being thrown for.

Standing in our family room, I noticed the answering machine's red button blinking.

"Kristen, this is your doctor's office in Reading calling. The doctor would like you to take your Profasi injection and come in tomorrow for your insemination. You're scheduled for 12:00 and your partner should arrive an hour prior. Call if you should have any questions." Beep.

"Oh my God, it's only day ten of my cycle, I wonder if there has been a mistake." Picking up the receiver I could feel the flush of adrenaline in my cheeks, which instantly felt warm and began to turn red.

"Blood Room, this is Jill."

"Hello, this is Kristen Magnacca, I just received my nightly instructions, which were to take the Profasi injection. I would like to double check that order, it's only day ten of my cycle."

"Hold on, Kristen," was the sharp reply. A pause. "I just checked with the doctor reviewing charts and they will see you tomorrow for the insemination."

"OK, thank you." I pushed the flash button to call Mark with the news.

Girlfriend to Girlfriend:

Keep a level log by the telephone: This is one trick that I was so happy to learn about. Because our business required Mark to travel extensively, the level log had a dual purpose. It gave me control to watch as the level rose and also gave us a little heads up as to when the insemination might be. (Hopefully you won't be experiencing multiple cycles.)

When the nurse calls you in the evening with your nightly instructions, if you speak with her directly, just simply jot down your hormone levels on a pad of paper (I left ours by the phone).

At our clinic, the morning sign in-sheet would have a space for the phone number where you could be reached, and next to the number I would write "please leave levels" so when the instructions were left on the machine I would have that information.

A ride into Reading on a Saturday is better than during the work week and I began to calculate backwards for the proper time to leave for the procedure.

"Hello, this is Mark."

"Honey, I just got my nightly instructions and we're to take the injection of Profasi tonight and have the insemination tomorrow at noon, thank God it's tomorrow and not Sunday, what would we have done? I have Sharon's shower scheduled for Sunday... I need to get as much done as possible tonight so that I can rest after the insemination tomorrow. I'm going to lose half a day, I don't think I can get it all done!"

"Kristen, it's tomorrow and not Sunday, I'll be home soon and I'll help with the baby shower, OK?"

"Thanks."

I proceeded to run around the house in a crazed state, picking up the family room, putting the baby tablecloth on the table, organizing the chairs, wrapping our gift, pulling out the fancy plates and dishes for the food.

When Mark arrived home, I looked and felt like a tired dishrag.

In our master bathroom I began to prepare the "Java spear." As Mark gave me the intermuscular injection, I held my breath and counted to ten and the ordeal was over.

Mark had taken over the responsibility of giving me the nightly injections. I was like the pitcher on the mound that pretended to throw the ball at the batter but at the last minute changed his direction to first base. I would balk at the last minute and pull the needle away.

At first I was upset with my behavior; for God's sake Kristen, you drew your own blood in Anatomy and Physiology in college, what's the problem? But I just had a mental block, and Mark stepped up to the plate.

It was a nightly ritual. I would prepare the injection, clean the area with alcohol, draw up the dilutant, and then push out the air in the syringe, yell for Mark, and sit at the edge of our bed on my side.

Mark would come in, sometimes rushed and sometimes "let's take our time," but would always do the same ritual prior to injecting the needle. He would pinch my arm and then give me the shot. I was slow on the uptake and didn't realize his motive for a while.

"Ouch! What's wrong with you?" I'd scream.

"All over!" he would say.

"You don't have to pinch me, I'll look the other way!"

"I know, I'm just changing your focus," he'd smile back.

"Well, change this," I'd snarl back, pinching his forearm. "I'm well equipped to change my own focus."

"OK, baby," kissing me.

"I mean it, Mark."

This process continued for all our cycles.

The nightly injections took on entirely different meanings for each of us. For me, it represented the culmination of all my daily work, the blood and ultrasound, and then finally the nightly instructions. It was all-encompassing for me. And to Mark it was just a job. Some days he approached it like a task, something else to check off his to-do list. This attitude really pissed me off.

I obsessed about the nightly injection being at the same time each and every evening. One particular evening, Mark was in a lengthy discussion with someone on the phone and would not stop talking. Entering our home office, I assumed the "hands on the hips" while glaring the "hairy eyeball" look directly at Mark. My behavior went completely unnoticed as he continued his non-stop talking.

"You see Joe Blow, yadda, yadda…" The sound of Mark's voice grated on me like fingernails on a chalkboard.

I marched into our master bathroom, picked up the loaded syringe, and then returned and took position in an upholstered chair in our home office.

To my total amazement, Mark spun himself around in his chair and stabbed me with the needle like he was stabbing his portion of a piece of prime rib.

The needle went so far into my thigh that it was not visible.

"Pull it out!" I screamed.

81

Mark, never dropping the receiver or his conversation, withdrew the needle and looked at me as though I had gone stark raving mad.

Tears swelled in my eyes as I flipped him the bird.

"I can't believe you just did that to me!" I yelled over my shoulder.

"Joe Blow, I have to call you back," was all I heard as I ran to our bed.

"That hurt like hell, you know that we have to have the shot at the same time each night, what the fuck were you thinking?" I swore at my husband, a rare occurrence.

"I'm sorry, Kristen."

"Now you have to give it to me again because the injection wasn't completed."

I truly hated him at this moment and he knew it.

"Ouch, stop pinching my arm!"

"All done!"

We didn't speak the rest of the night.

Girlfriend to Girlfriend:

I equated taking the hormone injection to taking a test every day that I had to pass. 6:00 P.M. meant 6:00 P.M.! With no exceptions!

If I was one minute late, I failed! The fear of failure was overwhelming and everything took on such life-or-death meaning – one mess-up equaled no baby. All or nothing does not apply here as I thought. Do your best; relieve yourself of some of your self-imposed pressure. If you're a little late, it will be okay!

Saturday, the day before the shower, Mark's voice bellowed from the family room. "Kristen, we really need to leave now for the clinic if we want to be on time."

"I just need to put the home fries away and I'm all set." I had managed to prepare all the shower food that could be prepared the day before.

"I'm in pretty good shape." I spoke to myself as I rearranged the refrigerator so all the food would fit.

The ride was uneventful and we eventually managed to park close to the door. This is an ongoing disagreement between Mark and me. He'll park the furthest away from our destination that's possible, while I pray to the parking god for a front row parking spot.

"Why didn't we just walk to Reading – that way you could have gotten the true furthest away spot?" The hormones did change my personality, along with my nerves.

"OK, Kristen, I get the point." Mark pulled into the space next to the door.

"I'm sorry, Mark, I was just thinking about afterwards, I could roll into the car."

We had been having a lot of awkward silence between us. Even my mother picked up on my mood swings, commenting she was never sure if I would be laughing like a child or crying like a baby. The hormones had a strong effect on me.

The Fertinex made my ovaries grow so large that I could feel them creating pressure on my abdomen. It was such a strange sensation, especially trying to urinate. I felt as though I needed to push harder than normal to alleviate my bladder's pressure. Those were my physical side effects. The emotional ones were even worse. I liken it to PMS to the tenth power. I was a mess emotionally, total "Sybil" behavior.

The Profasi went unnoticed. The shot left a puncture wound, but the effects of the injection were nothing. But then the progesterone – look out, world! I ate my way through the days to the pregnancy tests and would gain on average between six and ten pounds. This was yet another crushing blow to a fragile self esteem.

"Can't get pregnant, have to go through fertility treatments, and now can't fit into my clothes." Life was not good some days, and Mark knew it and would avoid me like a leper.

I entered the clinic's lobby and followed instructions and walked straight into the blood room.

"Kristen Magnacca, I'm here for my IUI."

"Just one second." The nurse turning to her list of women, the list was just too long.

"Kristen, are you sure you're supposed to be here today? You're not on the list."

"I specifically called back to confirm my instructions and I was informed to take the Profasi and come in today for my insemination." I was shaken.

"Let me get your chart." She walked away without consideration or empathy.

In those brief minutes I lost my composure. I was shaking and having hot flashes.

"You're not scheduled until tomorrow," she said as if I was stupid and had been the one to make the mistake.

It then dawned on me that Mark was upstairs in the spank tank producing a sample and if he had already completed the transaction, we would be in big trouble. Mark's sperm situation being what it is, Dr. Right had decided that we would only have one insemination every cycle instead of the norm of inseminating two days in a row. I was confused and panicking. If Mark had completed his transaction, would we have wasted our time this month? Or would they have to squeeze us in? I didn't wait to find out the answer –I just needed to stop Mark.

I was off like a prom dress, running full force to the elevator, pushing the button with all my might in hopes of making the door open more quickly.

Bounding into the IVF suite, I yelled to the redhead at the reception desk, "Don't let my husband take down his pants!"

She looked at me like I needed to be medicated.

"Is my husband, Mark Magnacca, in the back room?"

"Noooo…"

"Has he been here?" panting.

"Nooooo," soft and careful in case I was packing a gun.

"Well, don't let him take off his pants if he comes in!"

I swung the door open and ran to the elevator, jabbing at the elevator button until the door glided open and I jumped inside.

When the door opened, Mark and I were face to face.

"Where were you?" I yelled.

"In there," bending his head in the direction of the men's room.

"Thank God. Mark, they said that we're scheduled for tomorrow not today, what the hell are we going to do about the shower?"

"What? Slow down."

"I went in to give blood and the nurse informed me that we're not scheduled until tomorrow because they only do one IUI for us."

"Let's go!" Mark, red in the face, grabbed my arm and steered me into the clinic.

"Don't lose your cool, OK?" I broke down in tears and bit my inner lip to stop the flow of wetness.

"Can I help you?" The nurse looked at us with annoyance.

"I'm Mark Magnacca. My wife Kristen received her instruction to take her Profasi injection and come in today for an insemination, and now we're told it's tomorrow, what's going on here?" Mark was stern and more forceful than I could ever be.

"Just one minute, I'll get your chart." She scurried away. "You made a mistake, it's tomorrow."

The reply was not appropriate.

"No, we did not make the mistake, we have the instructions on our answering machine, do you need to listen to them?"

"No, let's look in the chart." She was annoyed and angry now. "It says right here, called patient and gave instruction to take Prof..." Her voice stopped.

"So, what happened?" Mark spoke loudly.

"I took the Profasi – what does that mean?" I was panicked. The nurse addressed my question first.

"You're OK with the Profasi injection. I don't know what happened, it must be because you only have one insemination."

Mark just stood there until an apology came. It was an uncomfortable, awkward moment.

"Tomorrow then? We need to be scheduled for the first insemination of the day."

"Fine, 9:00 AM."

Walking away from the nurse, my face was hot from the inside out. I was unable to cope with this situation and lacked the skills to break down the steps necessary to rectify the problem.

"We'll just cancel the shower." Mark swung into fix-it mode.

"We can't cancel the shower, we have all those people coming, and when would we do it again?" I cried. "I'll have everything ready and we'll call Aunt Sue and ask her to come and put everything into the oven for me. It can work, I think, oh God, Mark," I sobbed.

I hit the kitchen running and worked finishing the food preparations. The coolness of the granite on my arms traveled through my entire body as I reviewed the food list.

"I'm all done, I think. Mark, what did your Aunt Sue say?"

"She said, why did you schedule a doctor's appointment the day you knew you were giving a shower?"

"What did you say?"

"It was a mistake."

"So you didn't tell her that we are infertile and trying to conceive a child and need to go to the clinic to have your sperm injected into my cervix?" Being bitter is so ugly.

"No, I didn't tell her that." This answer came from the back of Mark's head. I watched as his dark hair shifted back and forth with each word. With that he disappeared upstairs, searching for the furthest space away from my ugliness.

The commute to the clinic two days in a row bugged me. At least the Sunday morning commute brought empty roads and a fast drive. Mark parked close to the door and we both went our separate directions. I chose my short button down jean dress for the occasion. It's appropriate for both a baby shower and an insemination.

I gave blood and then met Mark upstairs. Before I knew it, our time had come. I used the ladies' room and we went into the examination room. For some reason I noticed the energy in the room did not feel right. The nurse arrived and instructed me to push down to the end of the table and place my feet into the stirrups. My jean dress was snug around my neck by this time and my white legs flared open for the world to see my inner workings. The cleansing solution created the familiar sound of the cappuccino machine, and then the andrologist (a specialist that treats sperm problems) arrived with the syringe.

"Kristen Magnacca?"

"Right here." I lifted myself onto my elbows. Then the specifics of Mark's specimen were read and the syringe was passed to the nurse.

"You're going to feel some cramping..." Her voice stopped. The pain shot up through my vagina into my soul. I gripped Mark's hand. The pain shot upwards again.

"Whatever you're doing, you have to stop." I began to cry.

"Last month, did the other nurse have a difficult time getting through your cervix?" the nurse questioned.

"No." I had a sensation of my entire being falling off the table through my vagina.

"Let's look in your chart...the notes say easy, no problems. OK, let's try again." I felt like a cartoon cat, with its hair standing on end, being projected to the ceiling.

"OK, you need to stop! That really hurts!"

"I have to get another nurse." She was gone with no sympathy for my pain or words of comfort.

"Oh, my God, Mark, something is so wrong, I don't want her touching me again." I barely got the words out and the first nurse returned with a second one. Abruptly she barked out an order.

"You're going to need to slide down here."

My jean dress had twisted itself around my body so tightly that I needed to pick my weight off of the fabric and readjust myself before I could attempt to slide my buttocks down anywhere.

"I said you need to slide down."

I was totally over my head; I was struggling with my dress, my crotch, and my emotions all at the same time. I managed to assume the correct position and the second nurse pushed the syringe through my cervix and the cramping began.

"It's cramping," I sobbed.

"I'll wait a minute, tell me when it stops," nurse two said without emotion.

"It's stopped."

"All done." Her words threw me into hysteria. "Stay and rest for ten minutes and then you can go."

Never once did either nurse acknowledge my state. They turned and walked out the door. "Oh my God, oh my God, Mark." I could not regain my composure.

"That hurt like hell! What happened?" I stood up and the pain shot up through the center of my body again. Taking baby steps, I arrived at the ladies' room, emptied my bladder again, and cleaned myself up from the ordeal.

In the safety of our car I broke down. Reaching for the phone I began to dial my mother's number at her Cape house.

"I need my mom to come and help me with the shower, I don't think I can do everything," I sobbed while my shoulders shook along with my sense.

"Ma," I cracked out as soon as I heard her cheerful "Good morning."

"Ma, can you come? Something went terribly wrong with my insemination..." I handed the phone to Mark and began to rock back and forth in the front seat of the car. The motion of the car and the blur of the passing traffic and world added to my disorientation and dizziness.

"Lu and I will be there by the time you get home."

The sound of my mother's voice and the reassurance of her presence created a relief in my body that began in my shoulders. They sagged and pushed all the negative energy down out my body through my feet into the floor of the car. I laid the phone on my lap and turned to Mark.

"I can't believe this, Mark, I can't believe this."

Rubbing my arm, "Try to rest until we get home and then you can go straight up to bed."

The coldness of the window became the focus of my attention while I shut my eyes to escape the indescribable. My mother swooped in like an angel from above creating the effect of the Tasmanian devil. She went directly into the kitchen and rescued me.

I grinned and bore all the shower festivities. When the last family member left I crawled into our bed in the fetal position, mourning this day and the feeling of failure for all our efforts to fertilize one egg of mine with one sperm of Mark's. I felt complete failure, like building a sandcastle too close to the water's edge while the sun beats down, showering brilliance into my entire being, and completing the sculpture just in time to stand and watch as the water pulls apart all my effort.

This cycle ended in a negative pregnancy test. I will forever carry with me the conviction that my actions created the negative outcome and will wonder: If I had done things differently, would the outcome have been the same?

Girlfriend to Girlfriend:

I cannot stress this enough. A cycle is equivalent to a full time job. Do not take on any added responsibilities during one! Clear your schedule of all added tasks and focus on caring for your body, mind, and soul. Clear your schedule, put your feet up and be waited on! That's an order!

After much unnecessary pain and discomfort I decided that during a cycle I would opt out of everything – holidays, picnics, parties, gatherings, even funerals. This created conflict between Mark and me, so I would try to attend some functions if I had to, with my own agenda in mind.

Mark and I would have a code word or phrase so that he would know that I was about to break down in front of the group: "These pretzels are making me thirsty!" If he didn't get it, I would yell, "These pretzels are making me really thirsty!"

I would break down the function into parts. I'll stay for the appetizers only; if that went well, I would stay longer. If not, I would leave without feeling like a failure, because I had accomplished my mission of just appetizers. I gave myself permission not to go and not to stay if I had to go.

P.S. One more thing...We made friends with our andrologist and Mark and I were allowed to accompany our "sperm" through its obstacle course. We looked at the little guys swimming away through the microscope and then watched them being counted and recorded for history.

This helped me feel more at ease about there not being any mix-up regarding our specimen (which I'm sure there would not have been, but keeping in mind my state– it was a good thing to see it with my own eyes). It also gave back some control to both of us with the reassurance that this baby would still be half Mark's and half mine even though it had an extra boost from science and a crowd in the room when it was conceived.

So, ask if you can stay with your sperm... all they can say is no.

Chapter Nine
Art Will Definitely Make You Cry!

You have to endure what you can't change.
Marie DeFrance (1160-1215?)

"Ding-dong."

I watched as Mark stopped mid-descent while lowering himself into his chair and propelled himself in the direction of the front door.

"Trick or Treat!" sang into the air.

The cool breeze rushed by the couch as I pulled the blanket up under my chin. The couch cushions were now permanently dented into my form. There were no chances taken our third cycle. I had elevated my feet and they had remained in that position for approximately three hours. As the sun set, the trick or treating began and with each group of children, my husband's whining increased.

"Can I shut off the light? We're running out of candy!"

"How much are you giving out?"

"I'm letting them pick."

"Well, stop that!" That was the second time today I had said that to my husband.

The picture of Mark blowing up a rubber glove earlier this morning fluttered across my mind's eye. How utterly surreal. He had just ejaculated into a small plastic cup and the contents of the cup were sent through an obstacle course and fine-tuned. I gave blood and then entered into the suite and mounted the examination table as Mark began to fumble. Fumble with anything and everything not tied down on the examination room's shelf.

As the door swung open, the rubber cow's udder or rooster's feathers, whatever Mark was making with the surgical glove, was quickly shoved into his pocket.

After the incident with "Nurse I can't weave the syringe through your cervix" and a meeting with Dr. R., it was decided that in the future a doctor would perform my inseminations, and if all possible, Dr. R. himself.

Dr. Right entered with a great present.

"Mark has been touching everything," I said in a girlish tell-on-you voice.

Dr. Right just ignored the juvenile behavior.

"Mark, your numbers are great again, there has been another increase."

Mark nearly jumped into Dr. R's arms and immediately went headfirst into the file containing the poster boy numbers for "he man" sperm. The two men gushed over the figures.

"Let's set the mood." His voice was strong and suggestive.

Within minutes, classical music was wafting through the room and then the lights turned from blaring white to a soft glow. The mood was improving, but the nagging reality of still having an audience as Mark and I procreated was disturbing. "Are you done?" I asked, shocked.

"I could do it again if you don't believe me," he replied.

"I didn't feel anything," I questioned.

In that instant I knew I was pregnant. It was the strangest, most confident thought I had about my fertility in I don't know how long.

What's wrong with you? The logical Kristen now appeared, screaming, Snap out of it! The confident thought of being pregnant was never seriously considered; is it anywhere near rational to think the moment after insemination that you are instantly with child?

Where the hell have you been? shouted the emotional Kristen while the logical one replied, Here all the time, but you're deaf, you can't hear logic!

The inner sibling battling between the emotional and logical Kristen began again. It was so tiring.

Fourteen days after the insemination

Give me a D... Give me an E... Give me an N... What do you get? Denial. This time it came with a full course of anger.

The anticipation of my niece and nephew's visit for the weekend was just as strong as for the upcoming pregnancy test, which for sure I thought would be positive. But on that morning, waking with my niece, I found blood in my pajamas.

Fuck this! I am not dragging my niece and nephew to the clinic for an hour's ride to give blood and find out we're not pregnant. Fresh snow equals sledding.

And that's exactly what we did... we sledded up and down the great field in the forest. I ignored the pain in my side and chalked it up to menstrual cramps. We made a memory today as I began to erase the one that I had created over and over again within myself, that of a pregnancy and of being a mom.

Fifteen days after the insemination
Squeezing into the blood chair that resembled a high school desk with the arm on one side and the opening on the opposite, I began my confession.

"I stopped taking my progesterone tablets yesterday and I'm spotting."

"You know that you are not supposed to discontinue any medications until notification is given by a physician."

Yah, yah, blah, blah was how the lecture was interpreted on the inside but outside I was showing signs of affirmation, head shaking, nodding politely.

Glancing out to the parking lot I spotted two tiny sets of very pale white feet waving in the frigid wind through the back hatch of my car.

"Kristen, I strongly recommend that you take the progesterone as soon as you get home..."

The nurse's words moaned on while my attention was with my niece and nephew, and on killing Mark. I hope this nurse doesn't put two and two together and realize that those barefooted children outside in the snow belong to me! I had a vision of her calling the Department of Social Services and the slim chance of becoming a mother being stripped away from me like a banana's peel.

Rushing to the car while bending my arm to keep the gauze in place, I screamed to the oblivious Mark and my beloved niece and nephew. They scattered like leaves and began obeying my orders. "Close that back hatch, get in the car, put your socks on!" Finally, to Mark—"What were you thinking?"

"Their socks got wet on our walk and I didn't want their feet to be wet...so I took them off and have been drying them with the heat blower."

I just had to laugh.

We drove home to western Massachusetts with my cherubs and then to my best friend's first acting part in a local theater. My mom was going to stay with the little ones until my return and Mark and I would sleep over; my special time with them would be over tomorrow when my sister returned from her surprise birthday trip with my brother-in-law.

The play was a nice distraction and it felt wonderful to lose myself to some make-believe. As we zigged and zagged through the small college town to get to my sister's home, I reached for the phone to retrieve our messages.

"Kristen, this is your doctor's office, please call us immediately–beep."

"Mark, they probably don't want to leave the negative pregnancy test result message on our machine, should I call them?"

"You'd better."

My fingers walked over the telephone keypad with no instruction or thought. I had dialed the number so frequently that my hand acted on its own.

"This is Kristen Magnacca calling, I received a message to call."

"Let me get your chart, Kristen." It was the nurse from this morning, the lecture-giving nurse. Yikes, I thought to myself.

As the hold music filtered through the cell phone I fumbled with the cell phone cord, then, "Kristen, you are pregnant" filled the phone, my ears, and the car.

"What!"

"That's why we tell you not to stop any medication..."

"What?" Can you believe she is continuing with the morning lecture instead of the unbelievable news... "I'm pregnant—thank God!"

94

The car came to an abrupt stop while I listened to the emotionless voice.

"It is a low positive, the HCG level is on the low side, but it is indicating a pregnancy; you need to take more progesterone tablets and come back tomorrow for another blood test."

"Thank you God, thank you God..." Mark chanted while wiping away his tears.

"What does a low positive mean?"

"It could be something as simple as a late implantation, but we need to see a rise in the HCG each day. We'll see you tomorrow."

"Thank you!"

Mark and I embraced while the traffic outside the car sped by. Our prayers and dreams had been answered. We were pregnant. But the voice of the logical Kristen whispered, How can this be? I'm bleeding so heavily, how could any baby survive this much blood flow? I had even said those words to my mother, "No baby could survive this mess," when she tried words of comfort prior to my pregnancy test: "Some women bleed through their entire pregnancy."

I need to break this down into small bites. I'll take another test and then we'll determine our game plan.

"I don't have my progesterone!"

"No big deal, I'll drive home and bring it back to you," Mark volunteered.

"That's a three hour endeavor."

"It's worth it!"

He left with both of us in our stunned state and called me over a dozen times from the car. "I can't believe it! Are you OK?" was the question that was constantly forthcoming.

Day sixteen
A HCG level of 28.

Day seventeen
A HCG level of 108.

Day eighteen
A HCG level of 365.

Day eighteen in the evening
Dr. Right called.

"Kristen. You can now officially for the first time in your life say you're pregnant," he said.

"Are you sure…"

"Yes, Kristen Magnacca, I'm sure."

Returning the phone to its cradle I rested my head on the receiver and pushed my weight into the wall. I could feel my mother's stare.

"Ma, I'm pregnant, it's OK, the level rose again, Dr. Right thinks it's a late implantation."

Her look told her thoughts. The concern showed through her loving, caring glance. "No, Mom, really it's OK, I've stopped bleeding. Dr. Right thinks I was bleeding when the egg was implanting and you have to remember the progesterone gives me a super thick endometrial lining." I wasn't sure who I was trying to convince, my mom or me.

The week of Thanksgiving– a week and three days later
Tuesday.

"Mark, I think my large bowel and the prenatal vitamins are having a disagreement."

"What?"

"Look at my stomach, I think the iron in the vitamins are making me constipated, I'm not supposed to be showing already, am I?"

Mark looked my way while I was trying in vain to button my jeans. "Look, I can't even button my pants already."

"Try to have Raisin Bran, that should help; besides, I like it!" With a smile and a kiss, he was off to work.

I reached straight for the prune juice and began my "honey do list" containing the tasks that needed to get done before we departed for my mom's house the next evening. Mark and I had decided that we would wait before telling our entire families, but my sister and mom knew our joy.

Let's see, I need to get the secret ingredients for the meat stuffing and purchase the items for my dessert, I'll pack today, and then work on the food tonight.

As I leaned over the kitchen island, I felt as though my stomach was protruding. I still had great abdominal pressure and was having difficulties eliminating my bladder.

Prune juice, water, decaf tea, and more water. I was going to flush my system and help get things moving down there!

On one of my trillion trips to the bathroom I found blood. Bright red, heavy blood.

Panic washed over me as I raced to the phone to call the clinic. I was in such a state, I needed to look up the clinic's number. When I heard Jennifer's familiar voice, I rapidly began my story.

"Jennifer, this is Kristen Magnacca, I am six weeks pregnant."

"Oh, congratulations, Kristen!"

"I just came from the bathroom and I found bright red heavy blood and discharge."

"Kristen, were you straining to have a bowel movement?"

"Well, yes, but I have an extended stomach and the blood…"

"Let's have you go ahead and lay down and rest for a while and call us back in about an hour, it's probably because you were straining to pass your bowels."

I wanted so badly to believe every one of her words.

I went straight to our couch and elevated my feet. Lying perfectly still I phoned Mark.

"Mark, I'm bleeding."

"What, honey?"

My words were garbled by my sobs. "Honey, I'm bleeding! I called the clinic and they said to rest because Jennifer felt that it was because I was trying too hard because of the constipation."

"OK, lie still and rest and I'll call you in an hour."

I wasn't sure if the pressure and pain in the area were getting worse or if it was just because my entire being was focused on that area. I felt full and then an occasional pain, pain that mimicked menstrual cramps.

The emotional Kristen was in full, irrational ranting and overtook any other thoughts. Something is terribly wrong, what happens if I lose this baby, I don't think I would make it.

The time passed slowly but the urge to urinate came. I wanted to check again to see if there was still blood, check to make sure I was still carrying our child.

"Mark, you need to come home now!" I was in full panic. "The blood flow is tremendous and it's bright red and oh my God."

I curled up into the fetal position in our bed. My thoughts went nowhere beyond my stomach. My hands pressed into my abdomen as though they could hold onto this pregnancy.

Mark's voice traveled up the stairs into our bedroom.

"OK, I will have her stay in bed and we'll see Doctor Right for an ultrasound tomorrow morning."

I don't remember much after his words filled our room. The fear and pain took over.

Wednesday, the day before Thanksgiving

Sitting in the clinic's lobby with Mark, bending my arm after giving blood, I was numb, fighting back my tears and the pain.

I looked up and saw a woman who I had become friendly with – she walked over and I asked her how she was.

"I'm pregnant, Kristen, and I'm bleeding."

"I am, too," I replied.

"We must have gotten pregnant on the same day – we were inseminated on the same day."

The conversation was so far out there, so abnormal.

We had been first for blood and on the sign-up sheet for ultrasounds; the waiting was extended because all the doctors were having their IVF review meeting this morning. But I knew I was first and that we would have some answers soon.

The door swung open into the lobby and the nurse called the other woman.

No, I'm sorry, I'm first for an ultrasound, all is fair in love and infertility. I could not believe my reaction, I needed to go now or I would lose my mind... I had to know what was happening... I had to.

I was unaware how I got undressed and onto the ultrasound table when Dr. Right appeared.

His soft patient-side manner showed through.

"We're going to look at the uterus to check for a sac."

He gently and respectfully inserted the probe. He whispered, "OK, here's your uterus, and it's empty." I quickly glanced at the image being displayed on the little black and white monitor. It was a dark circular image.

"Well, what does that mean?"

"It's an ectopic pregnancy, your fertilized egg has implanted itself outside of your uterus. Depending on your HCG level, we can either give you a drug called Methotrexate, which will stop the cells from continuing to divide and then your body will naturally terminate the pregnancy by expelling the embryo."

My ears heard *baby*, not *embryo*, because to me it was our baby, my first child, not an embryo or egg – my baby.

"Or we're going to have to go in with the laproscope again and remove the embryo."

I felt as though I was going to be physically sick. I bit the inside of my mouth to fight back the tears; I knew if I broke just a little there would be no coming back to any sense of control.

"I can't tell if you're being stoic or if you're in pain," his soft voice whispered close to my ear.

I just looked back with a blank stare… How could I explain to someone else what I was feeling, physically or emotionally–I was pregnant yesterday, and today I'm not? How does that happen? How would a God allow this to happen? After all we had been through. This news was the shot across the bow that altered my entire being.

"I'll need to get the results of your blood work and then we'll decide the course of action. Why don't you go home and rest, and if necessary, I'll meet you at the hospital this afternoon."

Dr. Right hugged me and left the room.

I dressed in a blur and as I opened to door into the hallway, I started to break down; there was no way I could face the occupants of the waiting room.

Peeking into Dr. Right's office, Mark asked, "Is there another door we can go out of?"

"Sure, take Kristen out this door." It opened to the back parking lot and I bee-lined myself to our car. I wanted to run away, run away to the day before, when the joy of pregnancy and the anticipation of our child's birth was still being celebrated.

On the way home, the pain escalated. At first it was just increasingly uncomfortable. Then the waves became severe. I was breathing through the cramps and gripping the door handle. Knowing our true circumstances opened the way to me acknowledging the pain – previously, denying the pain meant that the baby was fine, but along with the truth came the undeniable pain.

By the time we arrived home, I could barely make the stairs to our bedroom. My condition was rapidly declining as I bent myself over our bed with my feet firmly pushing into the hard wood floor. I was trying in vain to manage the contractions, applying pressure to my stomach and the soles of my feet at the same time.

Mark's frantic voice filled the room.

"She's not good, Dr. Right, I need to get her to the hospital!" Mark was trying to mask his fear with a strong tone. "OK, OK, that's an hour from us, you know … I thought you knew we lived that far from the clinic … We'll have to leave right now, 3:00 o'clock surgery…"

I was hearing one side of the conversation and not liking any bit of it.

Mark slid open my closet and grabbed my purple overnight bag. I shifted my weight off of my right elbow and moved my head and shoulder to see him.

"OK, you'll need a change of clothes, some pj's and a hairbrush."

"I'm not staying over at any hospital, I'm coming home tonight!"

As Mark ran around our room packing my bag – which was a switch, he's never packed for himself, never mind me – I systematically removed every item he placed into the purple bag.

The pj's, the hairbrush, my make up bag were all scattered through our bedroom with my words "I AM NOT STAYING AT ANY HOSPITAL!"

The denial coping mechanism can be really way out there.

Mark realized he was losing the battle and said, "Fine, we'll leave with nothing and I'll have your mom bring you clothes tomorrow."

"She won't bring me clothes, because I'm coming home tonight!"

Another surge of pain interrupted my argument.

I gathered myself and the pain up and attempted to go downstairs; with each step the pain shot across my abdomen and through my back.

I managed to make it to the family room couch and instinctively knew that folding myself over the arm of the sofa with my head and hair dangling close to the floor and my knees on the cushion was the only way to ride the waves of pain. Getting back in the car in my state was unimaginable.

"I think you'd better call an ambulance, Mark!"

Within minutes our house was filled with firemen and emergency medical technicians. There was oxygen being placed over my face and someone monitoring my blood pressure.

Then this woman's voice whispered into my ear. "Hi, Kristen, I'm Chel, I'm going to stay with you and ride with you to the hospital, your body is trying hard to expel your pregnancy."

"You mean my *baby*," I snapped and quickly looked in her direction.

"I just recently lost a baby, I know that you're dealing with the pain both physically and emotionally right now."

She defused my anger directed at her and instantly built rapport.

"I'm going to speak with your doctor, your husband has him on the phone. Will you be OK for a moment alone?"

I began to huff and puff through another wave of pain.

It was as though the whole audience of people in my house was witnessing the loss of my child and discussing me as if I could no longer understand the situation or hear.

101

"Dr. Right, this is Chel, I'm the emergency medical technician on the scene. Kristen's blood pressure is elevated 160 with a pulse rate of 172."

"Oh my God, is it that high? We have to helicopter out of here!" This male voice bellowed into my family room.

"I am not getting into a helicopter!" I cried.

"She needs to be brought to surgery now," Chel's voice went on.

Her calm voice was once again whispering in my ear, while I could still hear Mark's voice on the telephone with Dr. Right.

"Kristen, I just got off the phone with your doctor and he and I agree that you need to be brought to the closest hospital. The surgical team is waiting, you need to get to surgery right now."

I had a shot of power! I stood upright.

"If I have to lose my baby, I will only do so with Dr. Right performing the surgery. I will drive myself to him if I have to, but I want all of you out of my house, now!" I was totally wigging out.

I walked into my kitchen; there were five firefighters in my kitchen, one reviewing my open dayrunner. Snapping the dayrunner shut, I shook his hand and introduced myself and then politely told him to get the hell out of my house.

Chel was at my elbow; sternly, she grabbed it and turned me to face her. "Kristen, I don't think you realize how serious this is!"

"Oh, oh, yes I do, I'm losing my child! I am certainly aware of the severity of the situation!"

"Kristen, do you want your husband to lose you? You're bleeding internally, we have to get you into the operating room *now!*"

I ignored her words as if she was reporting the weather.

I walked over and put a wash into the dryer... see, everything is as it should be, I'm OK, the baby is fine, and I'll just continue with my daily activities of life.

"Kristen, Dr. Right wants to speak with you!" Mark handed me the phone.

"Kristen, you need to get the hospital immediately; I have a close friend and her staff waiting for you, she's wonderful and will perform the surgery."

"If I'm going to lose this baby, the one you helped create, I want you by my side!"

There was dead silence, "Kristen, you're in danger…"

"Here, talk to Mark." I threw the phone across the room and fell to my knees.

The pain was overwhelming and my fight was over.

"Kristen, do you want to use the bathroom before we get into the ambulance?" Chel suggested more than asked.

I rose from the carpeted floor and entered the bathroom, the freshly painted yellow walls blaring at me as I put my head down and pushed out a trickle of urine while the blood flow was the force of a normal urine stream.

I gingerly walked through our family room into the front entryway and rested on the stairs. Then came the clang and cluck of the ambulance gurney entering my house.

"I am not getting on that! I'll walk to the ambulance!" My last act of defiance.

Chel held my elbow as I maneuvered the front stairs and walk and I began to climb into the seat in the back of the ambulance.

"Oh, no, honey, you have to get on the gurney now," Chel's motherly tone ordered.

I knew I was beaten. I gave in, and lying on my side, curled up into a ball.

The blur of the world whizzing by through the overhead windows and the siren from the ambulance burnt permanently into my brain.

As we sped to the hospital, I could feel my heart hardening and my spirit dying.

Girlfriend to Girlfriend:
An ectopic pregnancy is a pregnancy located outside of the uterus, most commonly in a Fallopian tube, and occurs in approximately one out of every ninety pregnancies in the overall U.S. population. A positive pregnancy test as a result from an

IVF has a 5 percent chance of being an ectopic pregnancy. I was totally blindsided. Just as I was unprepared for the journey of infertility, I was equally unprepared for the loss of our child.

The consequence of a miscarriage, ectopic pregnancy, early delivery or fetal reduction never entered my consciousness. I had so much feeling around becoming pregnant that I didn't think about how it would be to be pregnant and the risks that might be associated with it.

As previously mentioned, I encourage you to discuss this heart-wrenching topic with your husband/partner and commit something to writing in your fertility game plan regarding what your needs might be around the unthinkable.

I wish I had had the knowledge to bring this up with my Dr. Right. So I encourage you to bring this topic with your Dr. Right and ask him or her about it and how this might relate to you.

Chapter Ten
I Wish I'd Never Met ART!

Grant that I may not so much seek to be consoled as to console; to be understood as to understand.
St. Francis of Assisi (c. 1181-1226)

The great blackness was being pulled away from me as I was thrown back into my body. As I squinted back onto this plane, my eyes had a delay in focusing on the woman to my left. She was pressing on my stomach and fixing my blankets and sheets. Her voice caught my attention and vision at the same time.

"The embryo was at the end of the tube, you must have had PID [pelvic inflammatory disease] and it went untreated."

I managed to muster some strength and it took every fiber of my person to reply. "I am in fertility treatments, I got pregnant as a result of an IUI."

A clarity in my vision and mind began to size her up; she was young, a medical student or student nurse. She finished with her exam and walked away.

In my confusion and disorientation I drifted off again into the darkness.

There was an abrupt hit on the bottom of my foot and once again the sensation of being pulled back into consciousness. I opened my right eye, the light caused a knee jerk reaction and I closed it tight again. In that brief minute I thought I recognized Mark at the end of my stretcher.

Slitting my eye open again – it was my husband, with a broad smile and a nurse bearing down on him.

"You can't be in here! She just arrived from the operating room, she'll be in her room in thirty minutes, you can see her then." With a brief scuffle at the end of my bed, Mark disappeared.

My body began to shake uncontrollably; it was as though each limb had a life of its own. Then my teeth started chattering, my jaw joined in the spastic movements, and I focused my attention on keeping my mouth tightly closed, to no avail.

105

While drifting between states I felt my spastic body being weighted with warm blankets. "Don't fight the shakes, they'll only get worse if you do. They'll stop in a moment; it's the effects of the anesthesia."

I drifted again, feeling as though I was two distinct beings, the spastic body and the swirling consciousness. I felt as though I was trying to connect the two and was unsuccessful.

I awoke again, with no idea as to time or place and with only a vague recollection of the previous awakenings. I thought I remembered the catheter being removed and had a distant memory of the breathing tube being taken from my throat and being told to continue to swallow, but I wasn't quite sure if I dreamed those events or if they actually had occurred.

Next time I regained almost full clarity. The nurse was at my side with an orderly and informed me that I would be moving to my room. With an abrupt release of the brake, the bed started to move forward.

"We live in the same town." A male voice startled me.

"We do?" I replied.

"Lived there all my life," he volunteered.

"Oh, my husband and I love the town." I was surprised how strong my voice felt. The orderly and the nurse continued the conversation as we exited the elevator and entered my room. I was getting gurney sick from the motion of the bed and the moving elevator.

As we clinked around the corner of my room I stared straight into the darkness of the window. It was pitch dark outside; I had no recollection of the day.

"What time is it?"

"It's seven o'clock, you were in surgery for three hours and then in recovery." My mother's voice answered out of the dimly lit room.

"Oh, my gosh. "

The gurney stopped next to the bed. I instantly started to move myself, "No, little lady that's our job, you just enjoy the ride – 1, 2, 3!"

On *three* I was lifted, sheets and all, onto the new bed, rolled to one side and then to the other, the old bedding gone in a blink, onto the new sheets.

"Call if you need anything." The pair was gone.

"Well, ma, I guess I won't be bringing the meat stuffing tomorrow."

"Lu's already making it!" my mom replied.

With that the phone rang and Mark answered it.

"She just arrived in her room … yes, yes, the other doctor told us that … here, Kristen, Dr. Right wants to speak with you."

"Hi, Kristen. During your surgery, the doctor opened the Fallopian tube, removed everything, and left the tube open instead of removing it completely. It's a new way of handling this situation, leaving the tube in, but open. Things went well but they were very concerned; you lost a lot of blood and were in a lot of danger."

I was trying so hard to concentrate, but was failing. "Here's Mark again." I handed him the receiver.

As I gave the phone back to Mark, the doctor who had just done my surgery appeared. She was a pretty woman with compassionate eyes; she knew her stuff and her aura of self-assurance showed.

"That was Dr. Right," Mark stated.

"He was very concerned about you, Kristen, we all were. I do what he does, but here, at this hospital. He was actually one of my students."

She looked more like his peer than his teacher, I thought. Then she continued.

"You did very well, Kristen, but you lost a lot of blood. We were very concerned about you for a while. While I was in there I cleaned up some endometrial matter around your Fallopian tube; I could have done more, but we weren't in there for that. I left your tube open – before, we would have removed the tube, but this way we are hoping that it will reconnect and have some function. Otherwise, everything looked good."

"I'm sorry to keep you here so late on the day before Thanksgiving."

"Oh, that's OK, my husband already has all the preparations started."

She smiled and left.

I felt so overwhelmed, dealing with the physical and emotional pain of the loss of our first child, compounded by an intense spiritual crisis. "What doesn't kill us makes us stronger..." I felt as though this situation was killing me, killing me slowly. Looking back over the last hours, I now realize that God did send me angels along the way, first Chel, the emergency medical technician, and then this new doctor. But I still felt betrayed by him – how could he send us our child and take him away in such a manner? I wanted to break down but didn't want to in front of my mom.

"Well, Mark is going to stay here with you overnight, so I'm going to leave." My mom looked tired from worry.

"Kristen, I need to walk your mother to her car, will you be OK by yourself?"

"Sure."

My mom said, "When I arrived in the emergency room, the little lady who greeted you said she knew where you were, in pre op, and that she would bring me right to you so that I could see you before your surgery. She took some short cuts, I'm afraid I'll never find my way back to the car!" She giggled.

Leaning over, she kissed my forehead and squeezed my hand.

"I'll see you tomorrow."

"Mom, stay home, I'll call you when I get back home, OK?"

"We'll see."

I rolled onto my side; the cool IV solution sent a chill through my arm and through the rest of my body. I wanted to cry, but the anger took over. Why, God, *why?* What could I have possibly done to deserve this? I thought you were a compassionate God!

"Kristen?" The doctor quietly appeared again.

"Yes."

"We didn't do a D&C because there was nothing in your uterus. I just wanted to let you know that you should have nothing in your vagina for six weeks. I left your prescription for pain medication with the nurse and you should follow up with your Dr. Right in a few days so he can check your incision and remove your stitches."

I was still on nothing in my vagina for six weeks when she said her good-byes.

I wished Mark were in the room to hear this. Remember to follow up with Dr. Right…. I drifted off again.

"Hey, baby." Mark's voiced filled the darkness and was followed by the noise of the recliner scraping across the floor.

"There! Now I can hold your hand."

I felt the warmth of Mark's hand in mine; I started to pretend I was back home, in our bed, me lying on my stomach and Mark on his back, holding hands as we always do.

As I drifted off to sleep, my other hand found its way to my stomach. I was not comforting the area that had been abruptly opened and fiddled with, I was trying to hold in my longing for it to be a few days earlier, when I was still daydreaming about our child.

Waking at three o'clock in the morning, Thanksgiving morning, feeling dehydrated, I squeezed Mark's hand and whispered, "Mark, I need something to drink and to use the bathroom."

I sat gingerly on the side of the bed and then rose with a sharp pain through my stomach. Mark followed me into the bathroom while the squeak of the IV pole rattled behind me. The pain throbbing across my abdomen stopped the flow of urine; then I squeezed my eyes shut and pushed the remaining fluid out.

The cool tile floor matched the breeze rushing through the opening in the hospital johnny.

"Honey, I'm so thirsty."

"I'll go get you something to drink." Mark's shadow moved on the wall and I knew he had no pants on; his boxer shorts made a balloon-like image around his shadowed form.

"You can't go out there like that, put your pants on!"

"Kristen, no one is going to see me."

"Please, put your pants on."

With my pleading he flopped back into the recliner and pulled up his pants.

Within minutes Mark returned with his loot. Ice water, ginger ale and ice cream. The thought of eating made my stomach jump. "I just want the water."

"Can't let it go to waste," as he downed the cup of vanilla and chocolate ice cream.

The rest of the night was fitful; I just wanted to go home.

I woke the last time around 7:00 AM and rang for the nurse.

"I was hoping to have this IV taken out of my arm, they put it in me while I was in the ambulance and it hasn't been used, it's starting to bruise."

"Let me finish with the other patients and I'll be right in."

Pushing the button again, "I really need this IV out now, it's hurting me!" I was surprised at my impatience.

Within a few seconds the male nurse was in my room. "Let's have you rest your arm here, I'll go ahead and take both IVs out and get you ready for discharge ... There, all set, you can put your clothes on and I'll send someone to wheel you out."

"That's it? I can leave?"

"After the other nurse give you your instructions, you'll be all set."

He left and I immediately started to get dressed. What a sight I was. I had my old pink sweatpants (the elastic was gone so they were three sizes too big; they were the most comfortable on my stomach), an old sweatshirt, my black undies and bra, and a jean shirt.

"I'm going to burn these clothes when I get home, I never want to see them again." Mark just shook his head.

When the nurse arrived I was already seated in the wheelchair. I signed where appropriate and took the prescriptions for the pain medication.

Then this woman appeared to push my wheelchair out to our car. I was resting my head in my hands to not notice the other women on the floor, which I had a hunch was the maternity wing. I gazed downward and watched as the floor tile moved by, all the while talking to myself: A few more minutes and you'll be safe in the car, then you can let your guard down, just hold yourself together a few more minutes.

We had reached the front door of the hospital. I just needed Mark to appear and I would be free to lose all control and release some of this intense grief.

The woman's question broke my concentration.

"How long were you pregnant?" The coldness of the arm of the wheelchair mimicked her question.

"Going on seven weeks."

"Your first child?"

"Yes."

"Well, at least you didn't know her."

"What?"

"Well, at least you didn't know her."

I didn't have the ability to comprehend this situation. Looking up, I saw that the faceless woman was now shedding tears. My compassion was pushed forward with all the strength I had left.

"Are you all right?" came out, all the while looking desperately for our car.

"My daughter just recently passed away, she was 30 and it was totally unexpected, she went to sleep and never woke up..." Her tears flowed faster.

"I'm sorry... That must be so difficult for you."

"It has been, this is my first day back to work since then."

"Maybe you should go home, maybe you're not ready to be here...." I can't believe that I am comforting this stranger, all the while longing for someone to comfort me.

Where in the hell is Mark? I thought.

The long moment of uncomfortable silence was interrupted by the blur of green that was our car.

Thank God. Wait – what am I thanking him for? My internal dialogue was bitter. What are you thinking, God? Was this some cruel joke? Boy, I haven't broken her yet, throw her this? See how she can handle this situation? Maybe this will push her over??

I touched the woman's hand. "I'm so sorry for your loss."

She maneuvered the wheelchair close to the passenger door. I lifted my body, bearing the weight of my frame on my arms. I slid into the front seat and Mark shut the door.

As soon as the door slammed, I began to weep.

"You won't believe what that woman just said to me, get me the hell out of here!"

Upon entering my house there was a strange sense of loss, a sense of sadness. It was as if I was watching me through a different time. All my things were as I left them. My pillow was on the floor, the laundry in the dryer, my dayrunner and the cordless phone.... My clothes were still scattered across my bedroom and the lights were on. I felt as though something was missing.

I went straight into the shower. The smell of the anesthesia was still in my hair after washing it twice. I stood still and let the water run down my back. I had stitches in my belly button and a line of stitches lower down, forming a triangle.

My body was bruised and I felt weak.

I headed straight to our bed and lay staring into space. The stucco ceiling began morphing itself into demonic creatures in wait to take the last bite of shining spirit left in my being. The spirit that was so filled with belief, belief in God, in the Pollyanna philosophy of life, and in "God does not give you more than you can bear." Obviously that God hadn't been paying too close attention to my life over the past few hours.

The pain of my physical body, the pain of my soul and the emotional pain of the previous twenty four hours now blended together; there was no demarcation line, just the weight of each pressing my body deeper into our bed.

My glance shifted to the bottle of Percocets. I could down all of the little white pills... that would surely take the pain away... but wouldn't that take me away from Mark too? He would come home from the video store, movie in hand, and find a drugged wife, in what state of consciousness? Even in my despair I knew that option was not the appropriate one.

Our strategies of dealing with the loss of this pregnancy had already left their stations and Mark's was barreling down the north track while mine meandered down the south. He needed to escape into a movie while I needed to know what had happened during the block of time before, during, and after the operation.

"How did you find me in the ER? Where did you park the car? How long was I in surgery? When you came in and hit my foot, what were you thinking?"

"Kristen, we went over all this in the hospital! Your mom and I had a little something to eat, I realized the operation was taking longer than the doctor had indicated, I needed to see you and I found you in recovery, hit your foot to get your attention, and you awoke when they were kicking me out."

"OK, OK, but what did you eat? Did you cry while I was in surgery? Was my mom OK? Did she break down?"

"Enough, I'll be back, I'm going to get us a movie."

"I don't want to watch a movie, I want time back."

He was gone.

My thoughts scattered, trying to sort through the events.

I wanted to escape too, escape to a place of numbness. I had been trying to manage the pain without the painkillers, but then dove straight into them as a relief. My sister's nurse voice barked over the telephone, "You have to get ahead of the pain; take the pain medication and let your body rest, do you want me to come?"

"No, stay at Mom's."

Mark returned from the video store, movies in hand. "Driving just now, I felt as though I was on the outside looking into everyone's life. I feel as though we are the only ones alone on this Thanksgiving."

"Get out! I can't believe you're only thinking about this holiday!"

And so began the rapid decline of our relationship.

The day after Thanksgiving: Friday

I could hear my mom's voice "Helloing" from the front door. She had all the fixing for Thanksgiving dinner. Mark immediately started eating the butternut squash.

"So, are you guys staying long?" Mark's question surprised me.

"As long as you would like us to," my mom replied.

I was a witness to this exchange, not adding to their conversation, unaware where Mark was heading.

113

"Well, tonight is my high school reunion, I don't want to leave Kristen, but if you guys stay, I could go."

"Sure, Mark, you can call us when you're leaving the reunion and we'll leave then, that way Krissy will only be left alone for an hour."

"Oh, are you sure you don't want to stay over? It might be late... I could stay at your house and you could stay here?"

"Let me check with Lu." After discussing it with my stepfather in the other room, "Sure, we'll stay with Krissy."

Those words were the starting gun for Mark's escape. He ran full speed up the stairs, packed his bag, was down two flights of stairs, hopped in my car, and buzzed by the house in a matter of five minutes.

"What an asshole, I can't believe he left me!" My jaw was still hanging wide open. I spun around and my mom just laughed. "Here are the movies the asshole brought home yesterday; you guys can watch them – I'm going back to bed."

"Kristen, don't talk like that!"

"Ma, did you see him? He couldn't wait for you to get here so he could leave! He just left me to go to some stupid reunion! We just lost our baby, I almost died, and all he can think of is his reunion – he's an asshole."

I took my dose of medication and had a fitful sleep. Finally at 5:30 AM, I called my mother's house.

"Hellow..." Mark's voice was deep, the "I've been out too late and drank something I shouldn't have" voice.

"Did you have a nice time, dear?" Sarcasm melted the phone wires.

"Yah, it was fun."

"Get your ass home so my mother can leave!"

Click.

This incident was the first of many... numerous times I watched our car being driven by Mark with a mission... to escape.

"I have to get away from you, I can't get too close to your pain, you'll suck me in."

With that he would leave, leave me alone to deal with that statement and the pain of our loss and the physical pain of recovery. I can truly say I have never felt so alone in my life.

I remember reading somewhere that a man will do nothing when confronted with a situation he doesn't know how to deal with. My husband was doing something, he was getting the hell away from me, or running as if "Danger! Danger! Will Robinson!" was being directed at him!

One week after Thanksgiving

I began the brake test in our driveway. I would back the car out of the driveway, as I had done with the previous laproscopic surgery, and then pound on the brake to see if I could drive. Just as before, I would limp back into the house and lie on the couch for an hour after my outing.

The pain in my side had dulled but not completely disappeared. It was a nagging pain, and I wasn't sure if it was my mind and body in conflict, my mind trying not to move past the physical pain in fear that I would forget– not that that would ever happen – or if there was a problem.

I was unable to feel my bladder or feel if I had completed urinating. Every visit to the toilet, I would stand to wipe myself and still have a urine stream fully flowing over my clothes and myself. I finally called Dr. Right.

"Dr. Right, I'm still having some pain on my left side, but most disconcerting is the fact that I can't feel my bladder and I'm incontinent."

"Kristen, when the other doctor did your surgery, she left the tube open; it must have adhered to your bladder, causing your bladder to be in a constant state of 'fullness.' You're going to have to train yourself to use the bathroom again. I want you to develop your own bathroom schedule and use the bathroom every hour to begin with."

"Will this last forever?"

"It should get better...."

"I can't leave the house, I'm peeing on myself!"

115

"Try what I mentioned and we'll discuss it more on Wednesday when I see you to remove your stitches and check on your incisions, OK?"

"All right." I saw no hope at all. I will be the only childless woman wearing diapers – what irony is this?

Stitch removing day!

I dressed as if I was going to the prom. It was the first occasion to get dressed since the surgery. Up until now the fear of permanently soiling my clothes had kept me in baggy sweatpants, plus the pressure on my stomach was extremely uncomfortable. So for the big trip out into the world, I chose my elastic waist skirt and knee highs for comfort and chic-ness!

"Wow, you look great!" Dr. Right exclaimed. "I can't tell that you had emergency surgery. Is this your first outing?"

"No, I have been 'brake testing' in the driveway," I replied.

He looked puzzled. "What?"

Mark piped up. "She wakes up every morning and backs the car out of the driveway and stomps on the brakes to see if she can drive! I've stopped asking her not to!"

Shaking his head, "Kristen, why are you doing that?"

I just shrugged my shoulders and ignored the direction of this conversation.

"Well, I was very worried about you, I got the report from the other doctor and she writes that she saved your tube and that she did do some cleaning up of the endometrial matter. You lost a lot of blood, Kristen, are you feeling a little anemic? You might want to take an iron supplement and eat iron rich food."

The light bulb went off. "Yes, I'm so tired and still so weak, I think even if I could stand the pain from the brake test, I really don't have the strength to go out."

"She hasn't bounced back as quickly from this operation as she did the last one," Mark interrupted.

"This wasn't the same as the last operation!" I could have jumped down his throat.

This was the chasm between us: Mark felt as though it was the same laproscopic operation as the first one Dr. Right performed, totally denying the fact that we lost our baby, while I

116

felt that this was not even in the same hemisphere as the last surgery.

"I can't believe you're even attempting that so soon, anyway. You need to go easy on yourself for at least a few more weeks." Dr. Right's fatherly tone wafted across his desk.

"So, where do we go from here?" Mark was all business.

"Once you experience an ectopic pregnancy, the chances of a second ectopic increase."

Mark interrupted. "We cannot put Kristen in jeopardy again. It never occurred to me that I could lose my wife in the process of trying to have a child!"

"The statistical data suggest the chances are higher, that's why we have to bypass the tubes all together. I suggest for the next cycle we move on to IVF. If you remember back to after the first surgery when I said I wasn't sure about the functionality of the right tube, well, now we have to consider that the left tube might be damaged also. To be on the safe side, though, you might want to consider using some form of birth control to protect Kristen."

"You have to be kidding!" I nearly fell off my chair. Hearing Dr. Right's words out loud for the first time about the Fallopian tube situation made it real. It's not that I hadn't been thinking and mourning about the fact that I would not be able to "normally" ovulate an egg to its journey into my uterus, but now the cold hard reality was spoken and undeniable.

"Kristen, I would suggest that you think about it at least for the next few months until we begin cycling."

"I have not even considered having sexual intercourse and I really don't feel that I can even think about an IVF right now, I don't think I'm physically or mentally strong enough. Can we talk about this another time?" I did not have the courage necessary to enter into another cycle.

They exchanged a male glance that suggested it was some hormonal woman's thing, then Dr. Right's voice filled with compassion. "OK, we'll talk about this later, let's go take the stitches out."

I actually have no embarrassment left. Mark, Dr. Right, and I walked into the examination room and without thinking, I slid

117

my skirt off right in front of the two gentlemen. Dr. Right and Mark both looked extremely uncomfortable.

"What?" I asked, thinking it's not like we all haven't been together with me naked from the waist down.

"I was going to give you privacy." Dr. Right was still looking at the floor.

I just laughed as I folded down my "old lady" underwear, the ones that go so far up that the waistband rests on your shoulder blades, to reveal my belly button.

"What? They're the only undies I own that felt comfortable by the surgical site." My comment was directed at Mark's giggle at my underwear. "They're black, aren't they?" I thought that somehow the color made them sexy. How ridiculous!

"What did she do that for?" My belly button had one incision coming out of it at least a 1/4 of an inch long, while my other incision was hidden within the belly button.

"I wondered that myself, but they were in a real hurry."

With his thumb and index finger Dr. Right just pulled and out came the stitches. "I could have done that home!" My sharp tongue cut the air.

"Well, you're going to have to with this one, it's not ready to come out. After your shower, try with a warm wet towel and they'll just come right out."

Our heads were nearly touching as we stuck our faces into my bruised and bloody belly button. All I could think about was that from now on, when I look down I will see that scar and know it was from the day I lost my baby.

Getting off the examination table, I reached for my skirt and was dressed again within a second. The male uncomfortableness rose again. Can you believe it? They can stand and see me naked with my crotch waving in the wind and they're fine, but to actually see me dress and undress causes discomfort. Go figure!

"The bathroom issue is still concerning me, I have no feeling while urinating."

"Stay on the bathroom schedule and call me next week with an update. I'll see you soon." Dr. Right's hand was on the door as I went to leave.

"OK," I answered.

118

Then we looked in each other's eyes and for a moment there was silence. I was confused.

"You're not mad at me because I gave you an ectopic?"

He sounded like a little boy for a moment.

"You didn't give me an ectopic!" I answered, puzzled. That thought had never entered my mind.

Then we hugged each other for a long moment.

What's the problem – ART or me?

Mark was gone early and home late. I felt as though he were running from my neediness. I needed him in ways that were so foreign to him. *I* was the caregiver of the household. *I* was the organizer and grocery purchaser, the planner and structurer. And I was at a point where I was unable to cope with any of this... Hell, I was peeing myself!

His assessment of me was so mind boggling and so hurtful. "Kristen, you had this surgery before, what is the problem?" He would follow that remark with, "Last time...you drove sooner, you walked farther... you.... Last time... Last time..."

"Last time, Mark, they didn't take our child and I didn't almost bleed to death!"

"Kristen, it wasn't our child, it was in the wrong place, it wasn't going to live!"

"If the egg made it to the uterus it would have been our child, so, just because it started to grow in my tube, it wasn't our child? What was it then? Was it my egg? Was it your sperm? Weren't they together?"

The pain was so intense I felt as though I needed to defend myself both physically and emotionally. I was fighting with my soul mate and my Creator, all at the same time.

"You couldn't have just sent an angel to help that little egg get to the right place... No, God, you abandoned both the little egg and me! You left me! All those years of unquestioning devotion to you, the merciful God, and now this ...Why, God, why?!"

The tension between Mark and me was palpable. The unwritten rule that I used to look forward to every night is that we go to sleep lying next to each other and holding hands. After

119

my night in the hospital, this became a rare occurrence. I felt as though some energy force had lodged itself in my house, my body and soul, between my husband and me, twisting and turning and ripping up dust in the same way a tornado does to anything and everything in its path. This energy, rotating with such intensity, forced our normal lifestyle and feelings and beliefs so tightly against the outer limits that I felt powerless to regain access to them to stay on a course of "normalcy," if that makes sense at all. There were still there, but so thinned and weakened, they couldn't be pried off the sides of this crisis.

I no longer looked forward to our nightly ritual. I no longer requested that Mark join me to snuggle and debrief about the day or discuss our dreams. I had none and he wanted to be as far away from me as possible.

Everything was a grand struggle. I would fall asleep in a lonely bed and awake in the same position with that same loneliness. The comfort in holding hands to sleep was replaced by crying myself to sleep.

One particular night the telephone startled me awake. Mark answered the phone; it was only 9:45 P.M. but may as well have been 2:00 A.M. The call was from Mark's new business partner, who happened to be a woman. He took the call in another room. We hadn't had a conversation in days that had more than seven words in it, but when Mark returned, he began to tell me this story.

"Well, that was my business partner, poor her, she was having her nails done and it was taking too long, and blah, blah, blah..."

I lost it! I started to go hysterical.... Poor her! Her nails were taking too long to dry... poor *her?* I had had my body assaulted, our baby taken from me, I almost bled to death, and who knows if I'll ever feel my bladder again, you tell me to get over it, that I had this surgery already and should be back on my feet!

But! Great compassion because her nails didn't get done fast enough!

I urinated on myself from laughing... What does that send as a message?

Then the light bulb went on. Mark was receiving from his business partner what I was incapable of giving to him. In no way am I insinuating that it was a physical relationship, but he was looking to her for all the things that were lacking in our relationship. That's why he could provide her with so much compassion over an elongated nail appointment. But for his wife, nothing.

I seriously questioned if our marriage would survive this.

Girlfriend to Girlfriend:

The way that Mark and I coped with our loss was as different as night and day. Each of us carries our own coping mechanisms and, fortunately, up until this point in our relationship we didn't have to meld our two styles.

My reaction was clearly totally different than Mark's. I needed to talk about everything, rehash it and wasn't looking to solve anything, just to vent the tremendous amount of emotion.

Mark, on the other hand, wanted a solution to our fertility challenges. I'm not saying I didn't want that too, but I wasn't ready to address it again, and he wanted me to be "the woman he married." If we weren't going to solve the problem, he thought, what use was it just to talk about what happened? He has a real gift for helping people learn how to carve out their future, and I feel that this is why he had such a difficult time with my state. He was obtaining more and more consulting jobs and dates to give motivational seminars but then when he returned home, he felt lost as to how to use his skills and techniques to help his own wife. It was a constant reinforcement of how he was failing at helping the one person he would do anything for.

We were like two magnets with the same charge, being pulled in the opposite direction from each other, and the results were devastating.

I wish we had discussed what we expected from each other prior to our rapid descent into "ugly marriage land," but we didn't. We were also slow on the uptake to seek appropriate outside intervention. And I believe I failed at recognizing how truly bad the situation was getting.

121

So here are two things I would have done differently.

1. *I would have talked about what I needed from Mark, without assuming he "knew." Prior to this point in our relationship, if we prefaced any idea, activity or goal with "It's important to me," the other person had a red flag to the true meaning of what was coming. We did not use this strategy at all after the loss. I suggest that you create your own "red flag" word or phrase and put it in your fertility game plan. That way, a solution might be found more quickly to an impasse.*
2. *I would have sought out help sooner either from a family member, friend or professional. Unfortunately, I wasn't in a place to "hear" what the people the closest to me were truly saying. All the red flags in our relationship went unnoticed and the skills that Mark and I had implemented prior to the loss were not used, leaving us in a state of confusion. An impartial set of eyes and ears might have been able to make me aware of our present condition and provide much-needed intervention.*

Chapter Eleven
Reclaiming Body, Mind and Soul

The mind is its own place, and in itself
Can make a heav'n of hell, a hell of heav'n.
    John Milton (1608-1674)

The bah humbug blues

I was forcing myself to eat. Eat foods rich in iron and protein. But I was still so tired and most of all angry. I felt as though I was dragging around my body and behind it was this huge weight of anger. It pulled on my heart and soul, creating the antithesis of the Christmas spirit. There would be no decorations in my house, and surely no Christmas tree. Why would I celebrate the birth of the Son of God when he had a part in taking away my child?

Each previous year, decorating for Christmas was as exciting and fun as opening gifts for me. Since I am a bubble head and have no memory, I forget year to year what I have for decorations. So opening the storage boxes which hold all my Christmas treasures is just as wonderful as opening a new surprise.

But this year all those storage boxes would remain in the attic. Mark ran for cover around this topic. He broached it once with me and I came down on him like a ton of bricks.

"Honey, want to go for a ride and get a Christmas tree?"

"There will be no Christmas tree in our house this year! If you would like to honor the birth of the son of a God that took my child, go right ahead!"

Mark put his head down and backed away, zigzagging his way upstairs as if he was in the midst of war, shrapnel and heat-seeking missiles going off all around him. He found protective cover in our upstairs office, the door conveniently closed.

I was unaware of what Mark was actually thinking about my behavior. We weren't really communicating regarding anything. He would get so annoyed at my constant questioning regarding the events that led up to my arrival at the hospital, my attempts to fill in the blanks.

I felt as though he was walking on eggs around me, that he viewed me through some different colored glasses and really found the "Kristen" he was presently living with unacceptable and irrational.

He did not bring up the decoration topic again, but I think he called everyone else and rallied support. The telephone calls came pouring in. My attitude upset all those closest to me.

"Hi, Mom."

"Kristen, your sister and I are coming over Sunday, we thought we could take you shopping."

"That would be nice, Ma."

"And maybe beforehand, we can get your nativity set out and get your tree!"

"Shopping would be great, but I'm not decorating this year."

Silence on the other end of the phone.

"Your sister and I will do everything…"

"NO, Ma!"

I think Mark had called them both and discussed the absent Christmas festivities in our house. A similar conversation took place between Maria and me. But this time, a poinsettia plant arrived shortly afterwards, along with a follow-up telephone call.

"How are you doing?"

"Fine, how's your day?"

"Good."

"Thank you for the beautiful poinsettia plant, Maria, you really shouldn't have."

"Well, does that inspire you to decorate?"

"No, I actually put the beautiful plant in front of the fireplace in the family room and then put the gifts around it."

Once again, dead silence.

"Oh. I thought that would be a great starting point to encourage you to decorate, I remember how festive your house looked last year, you do such a great job…"

"It's not going to happen."

"Kristen, I just think it would help."

124

"Maria, I appreciate your thoughtfulness, but what would help me the most is another shopping excursion."

There would be no Christmas recognition in our house, no shining white lights, mistletoe, or any rendition of "White Christmas" or "The Twelve Days of Christmas." In their place, only great darkness and sadness.

A self-help Christmas eve

The only joy I did experience was purchasing special presents for my family members and Mark. I collected a lot of small, thoughtful gifts for Mark, and of course that one big one. There were the standard underwear and socks from Santa. A new outfit for work and play. And a toy for his age group. All wrapped separately to make our exchange last as long as possible for him.

"Here, baby, open this one first!" Mark looked so excited.

"Wow, and it's wrapped so beautifully..." Memories of last year's beautiful gold wedding band flashed through my mind's eye.

"*Heal Yourself through Exercise.* Boy, I've never heard of this title before ... OK, open one of yours."

"Awesome, a Polo shirt, I needed a new one of them! Here, try this one now." He handed me a similar sized gift.

"*How to Eat Yourself to a Healthier You...* boy, haven't heard of this one either.... Try this stack now," leaning over my crossed yoga style legs.

"New shoes, these are perfect, a new pair of pants, I love the feel of this sweater, comfy slippers...."

"*How to Journal Yourself Back to Health*—on tape!" Oh boy, I haven't heard of this book either..."Mark, what is this? The safety can and easy jar, so I can open things without cutting myself?"

"Yes, as seen on TV!" He was so proud of himself.

I just burst out laughing. I was longing for gifts that acknowledged my feelings of loss, wishing for a thoughtful gift of comfort or gentleness.

But instead, Mark's gifts shouted that I was broken and was in desperate, fragile condition. He was giving me tools to fix the shell of the woman he loved, but not listening to what I really needed – for him to truly be present with me. By "present," I mean to feel just for a moment what I was feeling, how I interpreted what had happened, and to understand how this affected me. To comfort me on my level. I longed for him to be there with me.

Maybe he was incapable of meeting my pain and understanding it. But that was the gift I was longing for, hoping for. Unconsciously, maybe I expected him just to know this, to know that I could move through these feelings of loss and grief and anger if my husband could just validate them. I projected that he was aware of what I needed and looked at me as being a weak person. He was handling everything so much more easily, with no outbursts, no breakdowns, and was certainly physically cleaner– in my depression, I didn't choose to bathe each day.

Mark and I were sitting in the same room, but may as well have been miles apart.

I made it through Christmas with several breakdowns in my sister's upstairs bathroom. The pain on my left side ebbed and flowed throughout the day. I was unaware how much it had been bothering me until my mom's comment.

"You've been holding your side a lot today, and mentioning the sharpness to the pain. I think you'd better be seen about this, it's been going on too long."

It never really dawned on me how long it had been; I was so immersed in pain that I wasn't keeping track, just trying to make it through another day.

A few days had passed since the holiday and we were preparing for our trip to the Big Apple for New Year's Eve. We would be seeing Mark's college friends and celebrating the New Year. To be honest, the thought of celebrating anything was a stretch for me. I was still in a constant struggle with my body and my emotions. Not to mention also with God. It takes so much energy to hang on to such anger.

"We have to have you seen before we go to New York, I don't want to go away with you in pain." Mark's words just droned on and on… We were in a constant state of bickering.

"I'll call today," with no real intention of doing so. What were they going to tell me? But as the day progressed, so did the frequency of pain and the pressure. The thought occurred to me that maybe this was another ectopic pregnancy. We had been intimate one rare time this month – with the pregnancy and my menstrual cycle being messed up, there was a possibility…. Was this just the fear of going through this trauma again, or was there really a possibility? Dr. Right said that my tubes were nonfunctional, the likelihood of pregnancy was slim, but the pain was so real.

By the evening it was unbearable again, the pain rose along with Mark's impatience. "I told you to call today, we could have had answers already instead of you being in pain."

"I just can't go to the clinic, the thought of another visit there with more bad news will send me straight to the loony bin."

"I'm calling, I should have done it myself a few days ago!"

Mark's voice was annoyed and impatient on the phone to the clinic. "This is Mark Magnacca calling, I'm calling regarding my wife, she had an ectopic pregnancy in November and is experiencing pain on the same side, it has been consistent and frequent since then. I need her to be seen tomorrow for an ultrasound… fine, we'll be there." Turning to me, "We'll just pack the car up and leave from the clinic tomorrow morning; it will add some time to our trip but at least we'll know something."

We set out early to be at the clinic for 8:00 AM New Year's Eve day. The sight of the clinic brought a rush of emotions, just being in the clinic's waiting room was unnerving for me. I stayed away from the area I sat in previous mornings by putting my back to the grouping of chairs. When the door swung open and the nurse called my name, I physically shook as I rose to follow, the scene was too similar and the pain too fresh.

Another Dr. Wrong was performing the ultrasounds. He arrived with a different energy than Dr. Right. His movements and manner were both quick.

"OK, Mrs. Magnacca, what seems to be the problem?"

Mark spoke for me and retold the happenings of the past few months. All the while, I nervously swung my feet at the end of the table and rested my elbow on the stirrup.

"Let's have a look."

There was no warmth to the exchange and his all business approach was difficult to understand, along with his accent.

I was unable to read this new doctor with no history of dealing with him, but the energy in the room was not good.

"Well, you're still internally bleeding, look at the screen, see the dark flow of liquid? Your tube is still hemorrhaging, it's going to have to come out."

His description was with no feeling, like he was reporting on an accident he witnessed, just the facts.

"Can you point out what you're looking at?" Mark's voice broke the reporting.

"Right here is the tube, the flow of liquid is right here, you can see it has a pulse to it..."

With the probe still inside me, I pushed myself up.

"I want Dr. Right now, get him in this room right now!"

His associate got insulted, "It's just a tube, anyone can take it out!"

"It's not just a tube, it's my tube and I want Doctor Right, NOW!" I was screaming. He left the room with no goodbye in a great huff! The nurse scurried behind him and then reappeared.

"I called up to Dr. Right, he's performing an IVF, he's on his way."

Alone in the room, I looked at Mark and cried.

"I won't make it through another surgery, Mark, I won't..."

He broke down along with me – he had been trying to remain strong for both of us, but he was overcome. "I don't want you to go through another surgery, Kristen, I'm so worried..." With each word his sobs grew stronger.

I wiped off the lubricant left from the probe and put on my underwear. As I stood, the pain grew in intensity and I doubled over. "Oh, my God, Mark, it's the same pain.... I can't do it again!"

128

Grabbing the pillow from the examination table, I folded it in half and then did the same with my body, squishing myself over the pillow and pushing the pain into the foam.

The door swung open and the nurse's words entered before her, "Dr. Right will be here in a minute, how are you doing, are you sure you're OK sitting like that?"

I didn't answer; I was focused on the pain.

The door swung open again and it was Dr. Right.

"Kristen, what happened? You were doing so well when I saw you last!"

I started to break down in front of him; it was too much to humanly bear.

"Are you going to do another ultrasound, I don't think I can."

"No." He looked down to the black and white images that were printed out from minutes before and continued. "I don't want to send you into the operating room again, it's too soon and it will be too much for you. I want to try a procedure upstairs in the IVF suite, the same procedure that we use to aspirate the embryos. It will remove the blood and relieve the pressure from the fluid and then we will go from there. Can you make it upstairs?"

"First my birthday, then Thanksgiving and now New Year's Eve – are all holidays going to marred forever?" Where that thought came from I don't know.

"You had a nice Christmas, didn't you?"

He totally broke my pattern. "Well, yah." Sniffle, sniffle.

"Let's get you upstairs and prep for the procedure. I want to let you know that if this doesn't work, I'm going to have to send you to the hospital and into the operating room, I have the nurse making the arrangements. So it's not a sure thing, Kristen, it's the first step."

I changed into a johnny, an IV was started, then I was given cocktail called "milk of amnesia" and instantly could not feel my nose. It was like an instant drunk, and God knows I needed one.

The room was dimly light and Jennifer was with me. Her gentle manner helped the time pass as I waited for the appropriate medical team to take their places; her presence was so reassuring. The anesthesiologist was at my left shoulder. He was a pleasant man with a deep soft voice.

"I'm going to open up your IV fully now and you might start to feel different."

I felt different all right; my mouth didn't stop moving. I wasn't sure if it was the medication or nerves.

"OK, honey, we're going to start, let's have you put your legs into the stirrup, that's right just like that, I'm going to drop the end of the bed now."

"Whee," came out of my mouth and no one seemed to notice. Did I say that out loud or to myself, I wondered?

The nurse carefully covered my areas that needed be flapping in the wind and then pushed the stirrups open as wide as possible.

"Who's there, girl!" No one acknowledged that statement either. I must be saying it in my head.

It was as though I was hammered – even though I was in that state of drunkenness, I already knew tomorrow morning there would be a rush of great embarrassment.

The room's conversation turned to New Year's Eve and everyone's plans. The two doctors said that they were attending a Big Brother function. Pushing myself up on my elbows I slurred out, "You have to go tell my husband about the Big Brother thing, he's thinking about becoming one."

"OK, Kristen," Dr. Right's voice acknowledged my comment.

"And, by the way, I want each and every one of you to sign an affidavit that I'm a real strawberry blonde."

The whole room froze, then the whole group of us bellowed with laughter. I knew I had made a total ass of myself and with the help of the "milk of amnesia" right now I really didn't care! It was a great high.

"Kristen, I'm going to get a catheter and empty your bladder, it's full and hard to get a good image of what is actually going on."

"OK, sssurrre." A marching band could have played "She'll be coming round the mountain" up into my vagina at this moment and I really would not have cared.

The other nurse scurried and got something wrapped in sterile plastic, there was paper crumpling and then muffled voices, followed by Dr. Right's voice.

"OK, Kristen, I am going to insert the catheter, let me know if you have any discomfort."

Then there was a huge gushing sound and all heads turned towards the monitor. The second nurse handed Dr. Right another bedpan and the gushing sound continued.

I could see the medical team making eye contact. I felt left out of the joke and wasn't sure if I had farted or said something else stupid.

"Great, I drugged her just for a bladder infection." I made out Dr. Right's upset voice.

"Kristen, it's not blood at all, it's urine–you have a whopping bladder infection. I'm going to get you prescriptions for antibiotics and Jennifer will help you get ready to go home."

Even in my drunkenness I knew that the other doctor was going to get a tongue lashing.

"I'll go tell Mark and send him in to you." Dr. Right left the room along with all the other doctors, three in total.

"Kristen, how are you feeling?" Jennifer's sweetness filled the room.

As instantly as I felt drunk, I felt totally sober and the harsh reality of what I had said made me want to hide. "What else did I say besides the blonde affidavit statement? I made a total jerk of myself!"

"Don't worry about it, Kristen, you were cute – you should have been here the other day!"

"I can't believe it, it was as though I didn't know if I was talking to myself or the whole room, I'm so embarrassed."

"Kristen, really, we're so used to it."

"I could just die of embarrassment!"

"Kristen, the other day a women was having her IVF done by the 'head doctor,' a huge man. In the middle of the procedure he asked the patient if she had any questions, she pushed herself

131

up on her elbows like you did, and said, 'Yeahhh I have one! How do you fit into your car?' We nearly died! He drives a Porsche!" We both fell into a fit of laughter.

At least I didn't insult the head doctor of this establishment; the only thing I did was make me look darn simple.

Mark appeared by my side. "Kristen, Dr. Right told me, I'm so relieved, I can't believe it was just a bladder infection. What were you guys laughing about in here? It sounded like a party! I could hear your voice all the way around the corner, you were so loud, Kristen!"

"Oh my, Mark, I made a total ass of myself! You won't believe it!"

Jennifer was giggling

"What made you think of your hair?" Mark was as puzzled as I was.

"I think it was because I was embarrassed about being in this position and then I thought well they can see head to toe and that popped out of my mouth."

"Dr. Right was still laughing, Kristen, when he came out of the room."

"Thanks for telling me that!"

I already had my New Year's hangover and none of the fun.

"I'm sorry about New York, Mark, I'm so sorry."

"Kristen, it's not your fault, we can celebrate the New Year alone. Chinese food and we'll get some decadent dessert."

Mark and I held each other as Jennifer picked up the remnants of the procedure.

"I can call the prescription in for you so you don't have to wait."

"Thanks! Did I keep you here?" We were the only three people left in the suite.

"No, I was scheduled to be the last nurse on duty, don't worry."

Jennifer and I hugged while I wished her a wonderful new year.

I fell asleep as soon as we got home and Mark ate the decadent desserts all by himself, watching the ball drop. It was good to see this year come to an end. Things had to improve. They just had to.

Girlfriend to Girlfriend:
Remember the saying laughter is the best medicine? I think it even applies even when it's drug induced.

I lost my sense of humor and the ability to look for the lighter side of my life. After the embarrassment of the "hair affidavit" statement wore off, I did think it was pretty comical. I'm not sure if things had turned out differently and I had to face another surgery, if I would have found the laughter in this situation, but the "hair thing" still has a life of its own between Mark and me.

So, my girlfriends, I ask that you give yourself a gift of joy each day and find something worth a smile or a laugh. Jot it into your journal along with the five things that you're thankful for.

The energy of laughter can change your perception and the endorphins will make changes in your body.

Chapter Twelve
The Dark Night of My Soul

...this one thing I do, forgetting those things which are behind, and reaching forth unto those things which are before...
Philippians 3:13

I began the New Year off peeing orange. It was a nice shade of orange, but orange never the less. I had expected it from Dr. Right's warning but it was still a shocker to look into the toilet and see orange crush swirling in the bowl.

"Kristen, if the bladder infection doesn't clear up by Monday, we're going to have to catheterize you." Dr. Right's words swirled in my head just as the orange water exited the toilet.

"No catheter!" I had yelled. "And I mean it!" There was no use.

"And one more thing...refrain from tub baths, no sexual intercourse for one week and don't use tampons for the next month..."

"I take showers, the last thing on my mind, and shit I can't use tampons!"

Mark and I did not need to be told not to have sexual relations for a week; the fact was that we were seldom in the same room together, never mind naked. Our time together was stressed and strained.

We both were dealing with the past few months so differently. I was angry, upset, depressed and hurting. Mark was indifferent. He thought the incident was just a lost opportunity, while I grieved the loss of our child. There really wasn't any middle ground to come to an understanding and that's what was happening – no understanding.

Mark's business associate and friend who also experienced infertility shared with him how she went to a mind/body clinic and what a great experience it was for both her and her husband. That became Mark's mission... to get Kristen into the clinic. Her mind and body needed some help!

135

I was open to his attempt to rectify our situation. To be honest, I could see the pain in my husband's eyes each time he looked into mine. "Kristen, I feel as though I'm watching you slip away from me and there is nothing I can do about it!" I appreciated Mark's words, but to me they just fell to the floor and vanished. Shrugging my shoulders, I would choose to not acknowledge Mark's comment. If I did, I would have to try to explain how I felt, and that had been previously unsuccessful.

We both had been so interested in books written by Dr. B who founded and ran the clinic and in his work regarding the mind/body connection. So to actually be partaking in this program was exciting, but I was still bringing the current depressed and angry Kristen to the program.

I was to have two appointments. The first was with Dr. D, who ran the infertility program, and the second was to return some of the paperwork and to have a physical. Mark cleared his schedule to come to my pre-screening.

I scheduled both appointments for the same day. At my first appointment, I instantly loved Dr. D. She was direct, approachable and mirrored back my feelings with great empathy. I liked her!

Prior to the appointment, I had been instructed to take a test to determine my level of depression.

"Kristen, you ranked pretty high on the depression test, meaning that you're pretty close to being severely depressed. That is actually a good thing; women who enter the program the most depressed usually do the best."

"My husband was insistent that I come to your program, he was the one who called."

"Oh, my God, it was your husband, Kristen? He was so cute, the office buzzed about him calling daily."

"Oh, I didn't realize he called daily, that's how desperate he is!"

"I have to let everyone know that it's your Mark that was calling, we usually don't get too many male callers."

"He's a good guy, sometimes."

"See you soon." She disappeared back into her office. I joined Mark for a brief moment in the waiting area and then I was called to the examination room for my physical.

I was so surprised at my behavior.

"I'm not taking any clothing off! I've had to for the past year and you're going to have to do whatever you need to do with my clothes on!" This statement came out of nowhere – I was comfortable with my surroundings and didn't feel threatened, I just was fed up with being poked and prodded. I was going to enter this group on my own terms. It must have been my control issues rearing their ugly head.

As I swung my foot back and forth, the doctor and the nurse practitioner took a step back. "It's OK, Kristen, if you're not comfortable with removing anything that's fine, we understand."

They then asked permission to perform each step of the mini physical.

I found Mark in the waiting area with his head in his dayrunner.

"Kristen, you'll never guess who I met!"

"Who?"

"Dr. B who wrote that mind/body book, he came over and asked me if I was being helped, then I told him about you being in the next group and asked him if he would mind coming back to meet you in a few minutes because you would be disappointed not to meet him!"

"Breathe, honey!"

Mark was so excited that he began to pace. I turned to put on my coat and Dr. B was standing next to me.

"So, is this your beautiful bride?"

Mark grinned. "Dr. B, this is my wife, Kristen."

"Dr. B, I love your books, Mark and I have been doing your 'quickies' for years now." I turned red as soon as the words left my mouth... they're not quickies, they're called minis!

"Honey, at your age I was doing quickies too!" His whole body laughed.

Once again I had made a total ass of myself. It became the buzz of the office and when I was gathering my belongings Dr.

137

D reappeared. "Kristen, I can't let you leave without telling you, you made Dr. B's day, he's still chuckling."

"Great!" My face still hadn't cooled down yet.

We had rescheduled our New York trip for the following day. The January New England weather turned ugly, causing a slight change in plans. We decided that to cancel again would be detrimental to both of us, so instead of flying, we drove one hour to Springfield and took the train into New York.

The strangest thing occurred with each passing mile and each click, click of the train. Mark and I started being nice to each other, actually talking and I felt as though I could breathe more easily again. In my mind this trip was a big deal; I was overcoming the fear of wetting myself in public. I thought, "What's the worst thing that could happen? I could pee all over myself and have people know that I'm incontinent. OK, how about just telling everyone that you're incontinent to start and always carry a change of clothes." That was my strategy to get through the fear.

"I'm Kristen Magnacca, and I'm incontinent." Mark and I laughed.

"It's so good to hear your laugh, Kristen, I missed it so much." His words melted some of my anger towards him.

Halfway into the three and a half hour trip, our conversation turned to our travel schedules. I put my head on his shoulder as he read me his itinerary.

"First northern California to interview that potential producer and then a little further south in California..."

"I'm going to both and then onto Arizona – Sedona, I've always wanted to go. Then for your birthday, I think we should go on another cruise – our first cruise was so wonderful, remember? The sun, wind, water, us getting engaged..." My words brought pictures of a different woman. I so wanted to be her again.

"I don't think I can go to Arizona, my work schedule is too tight."

"I'll go alone." It was the first time in years that I wasn't first checking my menstrual cycle before making any plans. If we weren't together during the prime baby making time, then we weren't together. I felt empowered… I felt good!

We arrived at Penn Station and hailed a cab. Jackie Mason's voice came out of nowhere encouraging us, "Buckle up and don't forget your belongings." Mark and I looked at each other and cracked up. "Your favorite guy!" I nudged Mark with my elbow.

I must have looked like a country bumpkin to the doorman who announced our arrival as I entered our friend's apartment building. There was marble and mahogany everywhere your eye looked.   The floors shined so brightly that they could have illuminated our way without the overhead chandeliers.

"I think we overpacked," I called to Mark over my shoulder with my finger still on the "Up" elevator button. With that the doors opened to a green marble elevator with a man in a leather jacket leaning close to the elevator controls.

My mouth fell open and "Hey!" came out.

I quickly looked to Mark and "Hey!" came out again.

My pointing finger and me looking at Mark trapped the occupant of the elevator. He started to walk past me. "It's wonderful to see you," I stammered out.

"It's wonderful seeing you!' he replied.

The elevator closed with both Mark and I on the outside. "That was Tony Bennett!" I yelled to Mark. He spun around and watched as the back of Tony Bennett disappeared around the corner. "Oh, my God! Tony Bennett!"

It was so exciting. The rush of energy from this feeling washed through my body. It was a new-old sensation. I hadn't had a rush of endorphins in so long, the excitement gave me a mini orgasm.

"Tony Bennett… All I could do is yell hey!"

We erupted onto Mark's friend and his girlfriend when they opened the apartment door. "We just saw Tony Bennett in the elevator!"

The trip ended on a totally different note than it began. Part of the agenda for the trip was to check out someone who does a motivational seminar similar to the one Mark did for our business. I was not totally thrilled about sitting through a seminar that was rote to me; since starting this business together, I had participated in the experimental board breaking exercise so many times and witnessed Mark present the seminar so often that I mouthed the words in the back of the room.

I went begrudgingly. One exercise was to take a few moments and do a brainstorm of all the things you would do in your life. My list started and ended with becoming a mom and improving our relationship. When the soft music was turned off, I leaned over to Mark and glanced at his paper. To my total disgust his goals were all work-related– our child or our relationship were nowhere on the list and apparently nowhere on his mind. I was so hurt.

Our elbows had touched as we simultaneously scribbled our lists, but our life together did not seem to be a forefront thought in his world.

"Where's anything about our marriage or our family?"

My pissed-off tone embarrassed him, and he looked at me as though I had totally gone off the deep end.

"What?"

"Look at my list, it's filled with us and our family, I don't even appear on your 'dreams' list, what the hell does that mean?"

I couldn't stand to be anywhere near him; I took my coat and sat in the back of the room. I wanted so desperately for him to acknowledge that maybe he was contributing to our difficulties too, that he was solely focused on his "plan" and lost to me and us.

The seminar concluded with each attendee breaking through a pine board karate-style, which I had participated in many times. The point is to identify a fear that you think is holding you back, realize how your life would be different if you overcame this fear and then use the pine board as a metaphor. Prior to breaking the board, you write the fear on the wood, and then when you smash through the board you are physically breaking your pattern and your fear. The music blared and the circle of people in my group was cheering while each member took their turn in the limelight and smashed through the wood.

Mark was right next to me. Our energy was not compatible–
he was indifferent and annoyed at me for my behavior around
the goal list, and I was crushed from his lack of empathy and
consideration.

When it came to my turn, the circle of cheering people
blurred together and began to rotate. I concentrated on the center
of the board as usual, took two practice hits, gently lowing my
hand on the target, visualized my hand erupting through the pine
and then released my arm and my hand – and all it did was
smash against the wood, making a slapping sound. It stung, but
not as much as my pride.

I couldn't believe it. I was blocked from breaking through
this piece of wood. Was it a metaphor for my life, being totally
blocked, by myself? Or was it the energy between Mark and me
that was interfering with the process?

I felt as though I needed to run away from him.

A touch on my shoulder and a foreign male voice. "Kristen,
have you broken your board yet? Then come with me."

I followed this stranger to the far corner of the ballroom, we
arranged ourselves quickly and quietly. I repeated the same
steps and then, as I unleashed my will upon the pine board, out
of nowhere my husband appeared next to me, breaking my train
of concentration, and once again I just slapped the board,
bruising my ego along with my palm.

"Forget it!" I shoved Mark.

"Come on, Kristen, I know you can do it," Mark said,
annoyed.

"Get away from me, Mark, just get away from me!"

"What's the problem?"

"Just break it yourself! Here."

In anger he grabbed the board from my hand, placed it
between the metal rails of the chairs we were sitting on and
smashed through the wood. The splinters flew through the air
and I flinched to protect my face. He abruptly picked up the
shattered wood and handed it to me and walked away.

I was so without confidence that this was the straw that
broke me.

On the phone in New York I sought comfort from my mother.

"Ma, I'm so stuck that I couldn't even break the board, I'm too far gone now, Ma, and so scared, it's a metaphor for my life, just as Mark keeps telling me, 'You're stuck and you're sinking.'"

"Kristen Agnes," I knew she was upset when my middle name came out, "listen to your mother. It's a board, a piece of wood, it doesn't mean anything other than for whatever reason you weren't able to break it! I won't allow you to say that about yourself. You're not broken and or stuck. You've been through an ordeal that you're still dealing with."

Sometimes angels are disguised as mothers, just as my desk pad states. I half-heartedly believed her.

The winds of change that had begun to sweep through my anger and depression at the beginning of our trip had ceased. We arrived home with no significant changes from our excursion. Only the blatant fact that we needed professional help was flashing like a neon sign.

The train ride plus the hour ride home took the last bit of energy I had left. I rushed immediately into the shower to rinse away remnants of the weekend.

I felt safe in the shower; the bathroom filled with steam seemed to hide me and my overwhelming failure and anger. The door was locked to keep my privacy and to let Mark know that I truly wanted to be alone – not that he would have sought out my company.

The rhythmic dripping of the water, along with its warmth, caused a release of emotions and stress. My forearm pressed against the back of the shower stall; I leaned my head onto it and began to weep. My eyes were squinted tightly shut with the entire outside environment closed off. I spun around with my eyes still clamped shut and let the warm shower water mix with the salt water of my tears.

Why God, why? I don't understand this! My inner dialogue slid automatically into my mantra of "Oh God, my heart is open to you... please come and sit in my heart." It was my mantra for meditation that had been pushed away through this ordeal. The setting of our master bath and the shower used to be where I would meditate on a regular basis.

The mantra sang over and over... until it was as though I was on autopilot and my inner voice played two part harmony in asking God a specific question.

Oh God, my heart is open to you... Why, God, why? Where are you, God? I miss our relationship... Where are you...?

I began to rock back and forth as my back pressed into the Formica of the shower.

Then, I thought I heard, "I have been with you always, Kristen. I've been here, you just haven't been open to hearing from me through your anger."

I collapsed. My mind, body and soul converged and then totally split apart. I sobbed and, still with my eyes closed, slid down the shower wall into a heap on the floor. My hair fell dripping over my face as the pressure from the shower spray seemed to increase with the intensity of my emotions.

I rocked back and forth on the floor of the shower, staying in time with the rhythm of the words from my mantra. Why, God? Why?

"Through this you will gain strength," came to me out of the darkness...

I was experiencing some form of sensory overload, and wasn't sure if I was making up the responses. Is that me? Then I heard my strong Kristen voice.

"Something good has to come from all this pain, God! The loss of my baby cannot go in vain..." I waited for a moment and searched the darkness for a reply.

"If I devote myself to helping other women with their fertility situations, God, will you send me a baby?"

I then changed the question to a statement.

"I will devote myself to helping other women in similar circumstances and you will send me my baby, God, right!"

There was no audible reply, no feeling or image, just certainty.

I took on this mission understanding that it was a verbal contract with the higher power.

I thought, I will write a book with all the information that I know now that would have been helpful then. I'll provide the companionship to other women that I longed for when going through my loss. My baby was an angel that can bring hope and strength to all of us childless mothers.

The next day, I began to organize my story. My journal was playing a huge part in the "Book" project. I was able to access the detailed images and events that otherwise I might have left out. During each free minute or break from work I would type away on the computer. It was a cathartic experience to get out all the feelings that had been pent up inside for months. I wasn't sure if this was actually a "book in progress" or a means to start to rebuild myself. I knew that the woman I had been would never totally reappear, that she was gone, but in her place would be a transformation.

But that night would be forever held in my memory as the dark night of my soul, where forces greater than I moved together to awaken some place not visible to my physical form, to recognize that I would learn from this, grow from this and use it to help others.

Girlfriend to Girlfriend:

Webster's dictionary defines depression as: "A condition of general emotional dejection and withdrawal; sadness greater and more prolonged than that warranted by any objective reason."

I just say it was my intense anger turned inward.

The part that scares me the most is I truly didn't recognize that my broken relationship with my God was a huge factor in my state of being stuck.

I wish for you the steadfast conviction to your higher power. To take time to listen to your inner self and "be" with that being that you call "God."

144

Chapter Thirteen
Reclaiming My Mind/ Body Connection

One cannot get through life without pain... What we can do is choose how to use the pain life presents to us.
Bernie S. Siegel

I hate being late! Mark, on the other hand, has time distortion and feels as though the whole world should wait for him, so he sees being late as some kind of strange thrill. Or at least this is how I interpreted his behavior.

We arrived at the Mind/Body Clinic for the first orientation session along with the other late stragglers and took a seat to the right of the room on the end of the second row. One of the reasons we were running behind schedule was that Mark needed to stop for a coffee and bagel.

"I'm hungry, I need to get something to eat, it will only take a moment." The time distortion thing again.

As I flipped through the black binder containing the class outline and paperwork that was given to us upon registration, Mark removed his overstuffed bagel and began to devour it. The cream cheese smeared across his face and he began to slurp his coffee.

"Wanna bite?"

I flashed him the hairy eyeball look and shook my head in response. I hated him at this moment. I wasn't sure why, but I did. Was it because he was chewing with his mouth open? Because he made us late instead of being on the early side so I could watch as the others filled into the room? Or was it because he didn't understand how I was so upset and hurt and that being in this room brought back a rush of emotions? Either way he wasn't my best friend at this moment and he knew it.

I half fiddled with the papers that were included in the program's packet and watched the couples interacting. I had the oddest feeling of recognition. I felt as though I was looking into my own eyes when I made eye contact with a few women. Their eye color was muted or distorted and in its place what showed was pain and longing. They were the eyes of a person who knows disappointment all too well.

Then this ball of energy roared into the room. She hovered around the food table for a minute, pouring a drink and then taking her place in front of the room. It was Dr. D. I felt the same as when we first met, I really liked her, but I was still angry at having to be in this room. As she arranged her drink and her materials, my ugly thoughts took over. Sure, other normal couples go to the movies and dinner, probably right now as I sit here with the other fertility challenged couples, glancing at Mark stuffing the last bit of bagel into his mouth! I wanted to punch something; this rush of anger scared me and I needed to get out of this room... But where would I go? Home to the pain and anger? I'm not going to even listen to this! I started to doodle on the edge of the papers.

Then Dr. D spoke. "Good evening everyone, welcome. Just to let you know, we are not going to talk about how bad infertility is because we all know how bad it is. We are going to focus on life strategies and skills to help you get through your situation."

I started to cry. I did listen to her words; although they were quickly said and then she moved on to the meat and potatoes of the evening, they had the effect of melting away at least some of my anger.

I had originally thought, What does she know? But with each statement it became apparent that she did know.

"... I want you all to form a circle with your chairs and then take a moment and tell us your name and a brief story about what brought you here and then something surprising about yourself."

"Hi, my name is Kristen Magnacca, and I'm fertility challenged." No one laughed; the image of my legs flapping open and my hair affidavit statement came flooding back. "My husband, Mark, and I have been trying to have a child for about three years now. What brought me here today is that I want to try to focus on the moment instead of wanting our family and wishing for our child. Just to be in this moment of my life.

"The surprising thing about me is that for 10 years I had a preschool/daycare center where I took care of 50 children a day. How ironic, it's the old water, water everywhere and not a drop to drink."

I looked towards Mark.

"I'm Mark Magnacca, Kristen's husband. What brought me here tonight is that I was hoping this would help get my wife back. I know that she is still there, but I'm losing her to all this pain and I miss her. The something surprising thing – I break pine boards with my hands and walk on fire for a living."

My mouth was hanging open while the tears fell down my cheeks. I guess I'm more screwed up than I actually admitted.

Mark and I held hands as we listened to the other members' stories. As each couple told their story, I relived ours. The pain of the others' stories and the heaviness of ours drained my being. Then we were given a "buddy" to call weekly and the first session ended.

We left the room and I walked at full speed about three paces in front of Mark. I was one angry women and my husband bore the brunt of the anger.

Grabbing hold of my elbow, Mark asked "Why are you so damn mad at me?" There were tears in my husband's eyes.

"Mark, I relived our entire last three years of fertility treatments, surgeries and the lost of our child all in that short period of time. While listening to everyone else's story ours replayed in my head. I just couldn't break free from the sorrow but I'm sorry I directed it all at you."

We left the orientation meeting with a "to do" list. This was a perfect strategy for me, since I needed to have something I was accountable for, checks and balances. We had already read Dr. B's book, which was the catalyst for the clinic, before even knowing about this program, but rereading it went on my list. I was to listen to the relaxation tape made by Dr. D and then was instructed to keep a journal. The journal part was not a big stretch for me; I have written in my journal daily for years. The last thing on my list was to keep track of me. It was a new focus and I was willing to try.

Hearing Mark utter "I just want my wife back" acted like a quick slap across my face. For the first time I truly realized how much grief my actions were causing him. I longed for the old Kristen, too. The old Kristen would have handled this a lot better; she would have done what she did with all growth challenges before: 1) Develop the goal. 2) Put it into writing. 3) Make action steps. 4) Implement the action steps. 5) Look at what she was doing and change the actions that were not moving her in the direction of the goal.

I was so stuck that I didn't know I was stuck. My self-protection mode colored the world with pain, and I felt as though I was in fight or flight response to every aspect of my life. Dr. D spoke about how women who are experiencing infertility have the same stress hormone level as women who are experiencing cancer. Was the pain and stress the cause of my physical, mental and emotional crisis?

I felt as though Dr. D was an angel sent to me to guide me through these dark days in an attempt to put some light into my life. But I was still scared. What if I failed at this? What if I could not regain that light?

Pushing those negative thoughts away while leaving the first session, I held tightly onto the plastic container encasing the cassette relaxation tape. It was my silver bullet. It had to be.

Just as the previous five nights since the orientation, Mark and I were settled on our sides of the bed. Dr. D's soft, reassuring voice wafted through the air. I was visualizing the path that she so softly spoke about and was just approaching the stream when the abrupt sound of a buzz saw interrupted the images. Mark had relaxed himself to sleep! It had been recommended not to listen to the tape in bed, but it was a nice transition from the hectic day to a sound sleep. For Mark, though, it was an abrupt transition. I immediately jabbed him with my right elbow, but the slurping sound of excess saliva and his grunt totally broke my focus.

I just laughed.

"Mark! Now you have to get up and rewind the tape for me, I lost my place." It was a release of stress and a moment of joyfulness that was usually lacking between us.

"OK, this tape really works for me!"

His boxer short covered bottom was waving in the corner of the room as he hit the button to rewind the tape. "Is this the spot?"

"A little more..."

"How about this?"

"Perfect!"

We held hands and my body jerked as it released the stress that was unconsciously stored within.

I wasn't sure if eliciting the relaxation response, listening to the tape or following the strategies from the clinic and being mindful were changing the way I was acting, but they were certainly changing my focus and awareness of my state.

Driving to Dr. Right's office one day a few weeks after I started attending this group, I watched the white lines on the road curving in the distance, judging the time necessary to move over to the right lane to exit the turnpike. I glanced down at the speedometer and then noticed my knuckles. They were white from the pressure of my grip on the steering wheel. Then I did a body scan and noticed that my jaw was clamped tight and my shoulders were ear high. I consciously took a deep breath and visualized a fountain of warm water washing over my head, down over my shoulders and then down my back, over my torso, forming a puddle on the floor of my car. With the water flowing over my body, my breath was through my nose and out my mouth, just as I was told to do at the clinic. "A mini."

A few weeks prior I would not have even noticed my deathgrip, never mind my jaw or my shoulders. I would have been unaware of but affected by my stress level. The mini was a release and a slowing of my body. I was thankful for the change and new focus.

I was especially thankful for the change that mindfulness had brought. I thought back to the times that Maria and I would "run for our lives" in the opposite direction when a pregnant woman would enter into sight. The pain that this woman brought along

149

with her pregnant belly went unnoticed on her part, but for us it was just another reminder of our childlessness.

I put my new skills into practice one evening when Mark and I were in a restaurant having dinner. Right next to us was a family of three. Two adults and one very precious infant. Instead of remaining focused on the family and the fact that they were able to conceive a child, a baby to hold and love, I constantly told myself how fortunate I was to be able to have someone else cooking me dinner and serving me a good meal. Otherwise I would have been cooking, eating and cleaning up! The longing was still there and I did avert my eyes away from the baby, but I was able to reframe the experience to that of a nice dinner with my husband, instead of leaving the restaurant in tears.

It had been a few weeks after completing the medication for the bladder infection when the pain in my left side began again. I feared that it was another doosey of a bladder infection.

I took action this time without Mark's prodding. I'll just go in and get another dose of antibiotics and be on my merry way!

"I'm calling because I'm experiencing the left side pain again and fear that it's another bladder infection or something. My husband Mark and I are leaving on vacation and would like to make sure that everything is OK before we depart."

"The doctor will see you early tomorrow for an ultrasound and blood work."

"Great. See you in the morning."

Girlfriend to Girlfriend:
The mind/body course was a life-changing experience. I would encourage you to look into this type of approach to help alleviate the stress that infertility causes. The stress management strategies that I briefly touch on do work and I encourage you to stay committed to the correct one or ones for you. Looking back now, I wish I had had more self-discipline and hadn't strayed from the strategies that benefited me. It was apparent to both Mark and me that when I brought my attention back to my "self" I greatly improved. Writing in my journal, doing meditation, eliciting the relaxation response, thinking abundance or being

mindful are all techniques that I was made aware of and implemented.

You can learn more about the above in The Wellness Book *by Dr. Herbert Benson and* Healing Mind, Healthy Woman *by Dr. Ali Domar.*

I encourage you to do so!

Chapter Fourteen
Letting Go of ART

In any project the important factor is your belief. Without belief there can be no successful outcome.
William James (1842-1910)

By some fluke of nature, the line for ultrasounds moved faster than the line for blood and before I knew it I heard my name called for this morning's probing.

Dr. G, who I liked, was on today, the nurse told me as I followed her back to the ultrasound room and went into the mechanics of getting reading for the "event."

With the image of my ovary appearing on the screen Dr. G. began. "Well, everything looks good. There seems to be a cyst on your ovary; sometimes that occurs, the ovulated follicle leaves a sac and that could be causing you to feel some pressure. Taking some Advil should relieve the pain and pressure."

"Should I bother with giving blood?"

"No, you should be fine within a few days when your hormone level drops and, like I said, the Advil should help."

I thought I had gotten off lightly. Just a cyst on the old ovary and I'm free to go.

The Advil did relieve the pain.

"Hi, baby, Dr. G. said it's a cyst on my ovary, Advil should relieve the pressure and it should decrease when my hormone level drops. How was your flight?"

"That's great – my flight was fine, I'll be in the seminar until 5:00 PM, I'll call you tonight."

For the last few weeks the seminar schedule required Mark to travel a great deal. Holding down the fort alone, my thoughts were more on the work that needed to get done than of me. I was strict about completing my homework assignments from the clinic and was committed to feeling the carry-over effects that Dr. D spoke about.

"You have to elicit the relaxation response daily. The effects will come gradually, we refer to them as 'carry-over.' They may go unnoticed but they will appear." Dr. D's words were my inspiration.

I was looking forward to Friday night when we would leave for our weekend at Cape Cod and another visit with Dede. My anticipation was spent wishing the week away and wishing for Mark's return.

"I see the bridge!" I won. It was a game that my family had played for years. The person who shouted, "I see the bridge," the entrance to Cape Cod, first was the winner. There was no prize for this feat, just the pleasure of recognizing the gate to our paradise. I guess you could refer to yourself as the "gatekeeper"!

Mark's family didn't have the same ritual so for him it was no great loss to not be the "gatekeeper." I was the excited winner.

We drove straight to Dede's for our Friday night appointment, gift certificate in hand. I had given it to Mark for a Christmas stocking stuffer. Mark's motivating factor to see Dede was to gain some clarity about his work situation, but for me, as always, it was our baby situation that I wanted some information about.

A secure sense of peace greeted us when we arrived at Dede's. We sat together on her loveseat and simultaneously reached over and gave her our wedding rings. We had learned the protocol of starting a session.

Mark began and their discussion focused around his work. She had pinpoint accuracy into the dynamics of business relationships and gave Mark information regarding his options.

Then the discussion changed to our fertility situation. I wanted her to "know" immediately and she did.

"Kristen, you are so tired physically. You really need to rest. Your pregnancy was stopped because your body would not have been able to carry this child."

"Dede, we're looking into adoption, do you have a feeling one way or another how our child will come to us?"

" I have a strong feeling it will be naturally."

154

I shifted in my head and the "doubting Kristen" appeared. There is no way that I will be able to "naturally" have a child – I'm damaged.

"Kristen." Dede's blue eyes bored into my soul. "I'm very concerned that you are putting so much pressure on yourself to have a child."

I instantly began to cry.

"It will happen; you have to let up on yourself and lose the fear around not having a child. It's so difficult for you."

I just sobbed.

"I have lost my way spiritually, Dede, you know how I had found such strength in God. This whole ordeal has taken me so far away from my belief system – how could God do this to me? I'm still struggling with a merciful God allowing this to happen, I had a conversation with him and feel that I am mending my relationship, but..."

"Kristen, it is really your fear that is holding you back and it needs some of your attention. You've experienced such trauma, you can't help but lose sight of your way. If you go back to your meditation and pray, you'll find comfort."

"I have been, with the mind/body course that Mark and I are attending, but I still have this hurt."

"Stay with it and you'll receive the answers that you are looking for."

"I think I am now!" I wiped my nose while Mark hugged me.

"Your son is with you now, he's coming to you, you just have to believe." Dede's statement caused another rush of emotion and I broke down in tears again.

"Good thing I'm among friends or the men with the white straightjackets would be pulling up!" I tried to laugh but cried.

The tears were a great source of release. I felt tired but lighter.

Then the strangest thing happened. A song that I used to sing in eighth grade church choir came flooding back to me: "I believe in the sun, even when it isn't shining, I believe in love, even when there's no one there, I believe in God, I believe in God, even when he is silent." I used to hum this song and sing it

155

to myself when it was raining, when I was single and when for whatever reason I could not hear God.

This visit did allow me to gain more peace and propelled me further down the road to a complete reconciliation with my God.

That night Mark and I made love with no other mission in mind but to reach the promised land, if you know what I mean. That had become my new mission. Our lovemaking had fallen so far from being lovemaking; the ritual of blood work and ultrasounds had changed me; the whole feeling around us being physically together had come to mean only "baby" to me. I would think, "Get the pillow, lift my hips, hope we are in the best possible position to give Mark's sperm that extra leap into my cervix, on to my uterus." The idea of an earth-shaking orgasm was far gone.

My mission for the days preceding our trip were to 1) develop the skills I was learning at the clinic so I could reconnect more fully with my spirit and God, 2) lose the extra pounds that the hormones had added to my frame in order to be "thin" for our cruise and 3) visit the sexual promised land three times a week. I would wear Mark out sexually now, instead of emotionally!

Mission accomplished! We both saw the gates to the promised land and entered together. Our trip to the Cape helped my mind, body and soul. I faced Monday refreshed and anticipated my next mind/body class on Tuesday. Once again being with the group of women who truly understood our current journey was a blessing. I felt stronger and braver because of it. I informed everyone in the group that I would miss next week's session because Mark and I would be leaving for our cruise. I was distracted from work with the packing preparations and organizing our summer clothes. The thought of warm sun and shorts was exhilarating.

Mark was still ping ponging back and forth between his dual careers. It was Thursday and the schedule showed an evening appointment.

"I'll ride into the office with you and drop you off, I have some last minute errands to do before our trip, our trip! Can you believe it's less than two days away!"

"That will be great, we can have dinner out together if you'd like and then you can drop me off," Mark added.

I had allowed the pain in my left side to be a mild interruption into my week. I was proactive and called Dr. G. again about it.

"It comes and goes, I'm leaving in a few days on a trip and nothing is going to stop me!" I almost screamed into the phone.

"It has to be that cyst we saw, just continue with the Advil and have a great time on your cruise, call me when you get back." Dr. G, along with the other physicians at the clinic, was aware of our loss and was greatly supportive of our taking a break from cycling.

"Kristen," Dr. G. continued, "where are you in your cycle?"

"Well you know the holiday rule, don't you?"

"No…" He sounded puzzled.

"That you have your period on all holidays and special occasions – the cruise falls under the special occasion category and I should get my period right when I put my foot onto the ship!"

He chuckled. "OK, call me when you get back."

After dinner, with the passenger's door open, Mark leaned over and kissed me. "Goodbye! Why don't you pick up a pregnancy test when you're out?"

"No flipping way. Do you know how much money we have given the stockholders of all the companies that produce pregnancy tests? There is no way that I'm increasing their wealth and wasting our money on another test!"

"For me, Kristen, please, it will give me peace of mind that we aren't having another ectopic pregnancy."

"Where did that come from?!"

"You keep saying the pain mimics the previous pain…"

I didn't want to argue. "I'll think about it."

"Please!"

157

I screeched into a drugstore to purchase birthday cards so that I could mail them before leaving and found myself in the "family planning" aisle.

"I'll just buy the generic store brand and get it over with and make Mark feel better." I tossed it into the red carry basket.

At home I became a whirlwind. Changing the laundry from the washer to the dryer, putting Mark's snack dishes into the dishwasher, addressing the freshly purchased cards and throwing the personal hygiene stuff into our suitcase.

"Did you get what I asked you to?" Mark's words startled me.

"Don't sneak up on me like that!"

"Don't change the subject."

"Yes, but I don't want to take the test right now."

"Well, when?"

I just resumed my frantic whirlwind motion and Mark left the room.

I was changing into my pj's and half brushing my teeth when the urgency to urinate interrupted my "three stooges" antics. I reached and tore open the box, and two tests slid out. "That's a surprise, I thought it only had one."

Tripping over Mark's shoes, I reached the toilet and held the wand in my urine stream. "I'll just get him off my back and waste the twenty bucks... I still have to organize our carry-on luggage, change pocketbooks, put our tickets in my dayrunner and... I think I'm in pretty good shape."

I placed the wand on our green vanity countertop and washed my hands. While turning to dry them, out of the corner of my eye I saw two purple lines.

Bending over with my nose almost touching the plastic, my vision was clear and two purple lines stared back at me. The image and my brain did not connect the true meaning. I stood up again and bent over, this time coming even closer.

"Oh, MY GOD! MAARRRK, MAAARRK, MAAARRRK!"

He was under the impression that he had lost the battle regarding the pregnancy test and was unaware that I had taken it.

"What?"

"OH, MY GOD! CAN YOU COME HERE?" I was dumbfounded.

Half distracted, "Where are you?"

"In our bathroom!" I was going into shock.

"What, Kristen? I was finishing something."

He walked around the corner through our closet area into our bathroom. I was standing, shaking, with my right hand outstretched with the wand.

"Oh, my God! Thank you, God!" Mark shouted.

We both sobbed and hugged.

Then I broke the silence. "Maybe it's wrong?" I whispered.

"Kristen, how many of these did you take that were wrong?" The male practical mind.

"It came with two tests." I spun the test around on the counter.

"Well, take the second one then!" Mark insisted.

"No, no, not now, do you think I should call Dr. G?"

"Yes!"

I raced to the phone and got the blood room. "This is Kristen Magnacca, I need to speak with Dr. G., is he available? Can you page him?" I was out of breath.

"He's actually sitting right next to me, just a second."

The hold music filled both phones, Mark was on the extension in the other room. "Hello, Kristen, what can I do for you?"

"Dr. G., I just took a home pregnancy test, and it's positive." I started to cry again and Mark took over the conversation.

"Hi, Doctor, I want Kristen to have an ultrasound tomorrow, I want to make sure we're not dealing with a similar situation to before."

"OK, come first thing in the morning."

"Oh – we're supposed to be leaving on our cruise, what do you think about that?"

"Well, you might want to stay local. The responsibility of taking care of Kristen would be with the cruise ship and they won't have access to emergency care if necessary. I would say you should save that for another time."

The cruise was not important any more, what was important was finding out if this pregnancy made it to the correct place, to my uterus, and if I was PREGNANT WITH OUR BABY!

I did not sleep at all and was up and showered before 5:30 AM. I took the second pregnancy test and once again it was positive. I needed visual confirmation of our pregnancy. We left the house before the sun was up and were the first patients for an ultrasound.

We entered a blue examination room with windows along the back wall. I was glad not to be in the room that still held my traumatic memories.

The thought of bringing a smudge stick, a bundle of sage and other herbs tied together to burn and clean the air, smudging out the old emotions prior to this ultrasound had crossed my mind. But that was not necessary, we were in the new room!

We were both dead silent. My heart pounded out the side of my chest. The nurse informed us that one of the other doctors would be performing the test, that Dr. G. was not in.

"Who's performing the ultrasounds today?" I knew that Doctor Wrong would not be performing any ultrasounds on me!

"Dr. H."

"OK, that's fine. Where's Dr. Right?"

"He's in surgery this morning."

The physician entered the room. She took the black padded stool next to the examination table. My chart was on her lap.

"Hi Kristen, I'm Dr. H., it's a pleasure to meet you. I was with Dr. Right when he was making the arrangements for your surgery back in November, we were all so concerned about you. Let's take a look."

I clamped my eyes shut and was unsure if I should look or not look... Mark's hand in mine sent strength and courage through my body and I turned my head to face the television.

Instantly the image of my uterus filled the black screen; there tucked in the lower right hand side was a sac. Our baby was in the uterus.

"There's your uterus, and there is the sac." The doctor manipulated the switches on the machine along with the probe.

"Everything looks great – congratulations!"

160

I cried, Mark cried and the doctor had watery eyes.

We took the day off and basically were in shock. As the day progressed, the magnitude of our miracle started to take hold.

I held onto the ultrasound photo of our baby. I sat and stared at the image and imagined our future. I wanted to be cautious about my feelings but I just could not be, it was already so real to me.

Maybe everything does happen the way it's supposed to, just like I once believed... I will need to wrestle with that another time. Maybe when I'm older or wiser I'll know the answer to my questions.

But for now, I'll give it to God and pray for his continued presence, even if it does go unnoticed.

Girlfriend to Girlfriend: Miracles do happen!

Afterword

What things soever ye desire, when ye pray, believe that ye receive them, and ye shall have them.
Mark 11:24

On September 21, 1998 at 7:47 AM, our 7 pound 7 ounce bundle of miracle arrived. Nicolas Armand Magnacca entered this world with his father's soulful eyes and his mother's strawberry blonde hair. (Proof positive that I do NOT dye my hair!) We decided to call him Cole. Nicholas in Italian is Nicola, which created the nickname "Cole," along with the insight from Dede.

I urinate on myself a lot less now, and have dedicated myself to my roles as mother and wife and to providing companionship to fellow fertility-challenged women.

My friend Maria and her husband Luke also became parents through their last attempt at in vitro fertilization. Their son was born three months after ours.

"Kristen, we did what you said to do and look – we're pregnant!" Maria said.

I looked at her with total blankness – "What did I say to do?" fearing that it was something outrageous.

"You told me to give it to God, Kristen. You told me to give it to God, so on our way to our last IVF, we stopped and blessed ourselves with holy water and lit a candle, and told God it was in his hands."

We both cried. We had always said to each other maybe one day our children will play together. And you know what? They do.

I realize that right at this moment in time your fertility shoes might be so tight and I know that feeling. I had worn that pair far too long as well. But I believe that, as the quote at the beginning of this book says, "Sometimes a moment's insight is worth a lifetime's experience" and hope that you have received that moment's insight and found comfort in my story.

I wish you all peace, strength and love on your fertility journey.

Love, Kristen

About the Author

Kristen Magnacca is a woman with a mission. For three years she experienced the heartbreak and disappointment of infertility. As a result of her experience she has dedicated herself to providing insights to other women and couples who are experiencing infertility.

Kristen is a member of the board of directors of RESOLVE of the Bay State, part of the national organization that provides infertility education, advocacy and support for individuals experiencing fertility challenges.

Along with her husband, Mark, she created and presents her seminars, *Strategies for Surviving the Journey* and *Your Fertility Game Plan.*

She has been featured in many media outlets including *The Boston Globe Magazine*, HealthWeek, WebMD, and The Health Network. Kristen was invited to testify before the Senate Appropriations Committee regarding her experiences to help raise awareness about infertility and the mind/body connection.

Kristen lives in Massachusetts with her husband and her son.

Printed in the United States
41814LVS00006B/202-210

9 781588 202130